Original Writing

from

Ireland's Own

2015

COVER PHOTOGRAPHY BY MICHAEL HARPUR

ISBNS
PARENT: 978-1-78237-954-6
ePUB: 978-1-78237-955-3
MOBI: 978-1-78237-956-0
PDF: 978-1-78237-957-7

A CIP catalogue for this book is available from the National Library.

Published by ORIGINAL WRITING LTD., Dublin, 2015
Printed by CLONDALKIN GROUP, Glasnevin, Dublin 11

Introduction

Ireland's Own, in conjunction with publishers, Original Writing, is very pleased to bring to readers our 6th anthology of the winners and other highly commended entries in the long-running annual writing competitions run through the magazine. This year's work is drawn from the 500 plus entries we received for our 2014 competitions and we are happy that the content is once again of a very good standard, indicative of the great writing talent out there.

Ireland's Own receives a great many submissions from our regular contributors every year, and we also receive a large number of unsolicited contributions every week, many of them of a good quality. We are only able to use a small portion of all these, but we do try to be encouraging and sympathetic in our approach as we are conscious of the great desire among people out there to get their work into print, and the small number of potential outlets available to them.

The anthology and our writing competitions are an essential part of that policy of encouragement and support. We thank Original Writing for their ongoing partnership which helps make it all possible. We also thank former Ireland's Own editors, Gerry Breen, Margaret Galvin and Phil Murphy for their continued involvement with this worthwhile project.

We wish all the contributors future success if you continue to pursue your writing ambitions; Ireland's Own is very happy to have helped you take these first steps along the road.

The short stories and memoirs in this publication offer a good flavour of what is available every week in Ireland's Own, the publishing phenomenon that has continued without a break since 1902. Our unique mix of entertaining, educational and informative features on song words, jokes, cookery, lifestyle and health, history and personal memoirs, also includes our old friends such as Cassidy, Miss Flanagan and Dan Conway, and a substantial section specially for younger readers,

As we have been saying about Ireland's Own for 113 years now, *The Week Wouldn't Be The Same Without It!*

Sean Nolan and Shea Tomkins,
Editors, Ireland's Own

You can keep in touch with what's happening at Ireland's Own on our lively new website, *www.IrelandsOwn.ie*

Editor's Note

I RETIRED as an editor of Ireland's Own last year but I am very happy to maintain my association with the magazine, having been asked to continue as organiser of the annual Original Writing Competitions, and as compiler and editor of the yearly anthologies.

I congratulate all those who have made it into this year's production, including quite a few regulars, and especially those of you who are being published in a book for the first time. I thank you all for your help and co-operation and I hope you feel pleased and happy with the end result. Well done also to the hundreds of others who entered; perhaps your turn will come in next year's anthology.

A special word of thanks to Billy Roche, Wexford novelist, playwright, screenplay and short story writer, for providing a foreword for this year's edition; your support and encouragement is greatly appreciated by us, and also by all the writers.

I thank Original Writing for their continued sponsorship, especially Martin Delany, Steven Weekes, Niamh Gallagher and their team, and I also thank Sean Nolan and Shea Tomkins of Ireland's Own for their ongoing help and support.

Phil Murphy,
September 2015.

Original Writing

Original Writing Limited has had a connection with Ireland's Own for a number of years, both as sponsor of the magazine's writing competitions and as publisher of the 'Original Writing From Ireland's Own'. Over the years, there have been many wonderful entries and we would like to take this opportunity to congratulate all of the winners and other authors, whose writings are contained in this anthology. Each year, we take great pleasure in producing an anthology of work that contains the voices of so many new and exciting writers.

Original Writing Limited offers many different publishing, printing and eBook services, which may be of particular interest to readers of Ireland's Own, who write in their spare time or have family members or friends who write.

Original Writing provides writers the opportunity to have their collected works in a paperback or hardback of bookshop quality with a full colour cover, to distribute to family, friends and colleagues. Page counts can be as low as twenty for paperbacks and orders are accepted from five copies. Prices start at €2.50 per paperback copy.

Aside from print books, we also offer great packages for those interested in digital publishing. The market for eBooks is growing at a tremendous rate and we offer a conversion and listing service which will get the author's book listed on over 900 websites around the world.

We also offer various services in social media training and websites for writers, in order to help you reach more potential readers and connect with them. Use our simple website builder to create a stylish, affordable and easily manageable online showcase for your work.

For any enquiries about our printing, eBook or Writer's Services, please contact Original Writing Limited at 01-6174834 or info@originalwriting.ie. Further details and a full list of all our writers' works are also available at www.originalwriting.ie

Foreword

By Billy Roche

Award winning Wexford-born playwright, novelist, short story and screenplay writer, stage and screen actor, and musician.

'COMEDY is no laughing matter,' someone once wrote, and I'd like to add my own tuppence worth to that statement and coin the phrase: *Writing in no talking matter.* So many would-be writers appear to talk their stories out of existence, they talk and talk and think and tell all until there is nothing left to say.

No, '*Save you passion for the page,*' is the wise old adage. Talking is cheap and so if you want to write seriously you must stop talking and go home to your own house and sit down and begin to write and re-write and chop and change until the job gets done. Of course first you will have to determine whether or not you are a real storyteller to begin with.

No, not everybody is – after all, just because you can whistle doesn't mean you can sing. (A Storyteller is someone who can go to the corner shop and come back with an interesting yarn to tell.) But, let's give you the benefit of the doubt and agree that you have the gift, then, you will have to bite the bullet and apply yourself to the task in hand- the telling of a tale.

And if you do persist and manage to get to the other side of the river then you will soon realise that you are only halfway there. I say, 'halfway there,' because after the writing comes the essential part of the operation- the selling. Phil Lynott once remarked that almost anyone can write a song, but not everyone has the wherewithal to sell it.

He went on to relate how he once flew to Luxembourg so he could put a record directly into the hands of a particular radio DJ. Yes, he knew how to sell a song, Phil, and he was willing to go to great lengths to do it. You, of course, do not have to fly to Luxembourg, but you will have to shop around. Thankfully there are many avenues nowadays:

magazines and journals and competitions and workshops-at home and abroad.

And there's Ireland's Own, one of the most widely read journals in this hemisphere, which mercifully provides outlets for all sorts of writing: from the comic to the ironic to the tragic, from reality to fiction – short stories, memoirs, skits, jokes, recipes and fantastic fables, the whole gambit. And they run annual writing competitions, with the end results being anthologies like this one.

To know the magazine is still there is comforting to say the least. And if you do manage to get a piece into the writing competitions shortlist, then, chances are (and this is the bonus), its inclusion in the anthology may follow, and knowing one can lead to the other is a journey well worth travelling.

I'd like to congratulate all those who made it inside the book and great praise goes to book editor Phil Murphy, and to magazine editors Sean Nolan and Shea Tomkins who are keeping the great Ireland's Own tradition alive. The book looks and feels and reads first rate, it is a great achievement!

If you already have a story in this anthology then you know the drill. If you are not amongst the contributors and you'd like to be, then might I suggest that you follow the above instructions: stop talking and go home and sit down and begin the Beguine. In the meantime, I'm off to patent the phrase: Writing is no talking matter!

Billy Roche.

Editor: *Billy Roche began his career as a singer/musician with The Roach Band; he achieved great success with his Wexford Trilogy of plays, winners of stage awards, and also produced on TV; he has written a number of other plays, a novel (Tumbling Down) and a book of short stories (Tales from Rainwater Pond). He has acted on stage and screen, written screenplays and written a crime series screened on RTE Television in Autumn 2015 entitled 'Clean Break'.*

Contents

Competition Winners

Highly Commended

Overall Open Short Story Winner

LETTING GO

BY TINA SWEENEY
Enniscorthy, Co. Wexford.

A mother is dealing with her youngest child heading off to secondary school, facing into a whole new world, while she fusses and worries and ponders her own future ...

LONG BEFORE the alarm clock rings I am awake. A nervous excitement has been dancing in my stomach since dawn, making sleep as impossible as breakfast. At last it's here, this day we have been planning for and working towards for months, crossing off days on the calendar with a mixture of anticipation and dread.

It is a relief when the alarm finally goes off and I can jump out of bed. It is time to begin. I shake my husband gently, getting impatient as he continues to snore. "Come on, honey, it's time to get up."

"What?" he mumbles sleepily. "Has the alarm gone off?"

I dress quickly in tee-shirt and jeans, running a quick brush through my short blonde hair. Seeing my husband's dark head still buried in the pillows, I nudge him again.

"John, will you get up and be early for once? Tommy will need you this morning."

"Oh yeah, right, sorry, I forgot about that," comes the muffled reply, and I wonder as I run downstairs how anyone in this house could have forgotten what is happening this morning!

I get breakfast ready before I call Tommy. Of course at thirteen he is big enough to get his own breakfast, but I rationalise that today is a special day, and I'm just helping him to get ready on time. A quick glance at the kitchen clock has me hurrying back upstairs to tap on his bedroom door. I wait for his quiet "Come in" – another new regime we're both getting used to! Like me, he has been awake for a while.

"Time to get up, Tommy," I smile reassuringly. "How are you feeling this morning?"

"Fine," he answers quickly. "And it's 'Tom' now, remember?"

"Oh yes, sorry, I forgot. I promise I'll remember in future!"

Looking at him in the bed, his tousled blond curls surrounding a still-childish face, I can't help thinking that he's still my little boy. But I know as soon as he gets out of bed the illusion will be shattered. He now stands shoulder to shoulder with me, and joyfully declares to everyone that he is no longer the smallest person in the house. How strange it feels after so many years of stooping down to little ones to realise I now hold that title!

Perching on the side of his bed, I brush his curls out of his eyes. "Well, are you all set for the big day?" I ask.

"Sure. It'll be great, Mam. I wonder if I'll be the tallest in the class."

His grin is infectious. "You might be," I admit, leaning over and planting a kiss on his cheek.

"Ah Mam!" he squeals in protest, squirming away and jumping out of bed.

"Sorry," I laugh regretfully. "I couldn't help myself. You just looked so cute, lying there in bed!"

I go over to the wardrobe and take out the new uniform. Navy and grey, it seems sombre and grown-up after the bright green of primary school. It looks too big, as if it cannot possibly be the right size, but I know that everything has been carefully measured and adjusted, so it will fit perfectly. Just as I know that Tommy is ready for secondary school. It is I who am not ready.

I leave him to get dressed, crossing the landing to thump noisily on his older brother's door.

"Luke, are you up? Don't forget, its Tommy's first day. You can't be late for the bus today!"

I laugh my way downstairs as Luke's "Ok" clashes with Tommy's "It's Tom – *Tom's* first day!"

"It's too early in the morning to be coping with teenagers," I mutter as I fill the kettle, desperate for coffee.

Waiting for the kettle to boil, my mind drifts back to Luke's first day in secondary school – four years ago now, but it seems like only yesterday. How quickly the time has passed. Now he towers over me and considers the smallest piece of advice completely superfluous. What would I know? I can't even navigate an iphone!

I remember his nervousness on that first morning, and how he struggled to stand upright under the weight of his new schoolbag. Now he's so laid-back about everything that he regularly misses the bus in the morning and I have to drive him in to school.

"Make him walk," is his father's advice, which I ignore, even though I know he is right. Next year Luke will be off to college – he'll have to get himself up on time then. But I can't think about college this morning. I can only let go a little at a time. I stir an extra spoon of coffee into the steaming mug – today I need all the help I can get!

The boys erupt into the kitchen, squabbling as usual. Luke and I speak to each other in looks behind Tommy's back. My look says "Didn't I ask you to be nice to him this morning?"

And his look says "I am being nice!"

We've had this conversation before, a million times, in words as well as looks. My female mind still struggles with the male concept of helping by not helping and comforting with a punch in the shoulder.

With relief I hear John coming down the stairs. I escape, taking my coffee outside to the patio, leaving him to sort it out. I know that whatever fatherly advice gets passed on will be more valuable this morning than anything I can offer.

"Hey Tom, how's that new phone going?" John's deep tones follow me out.

"Great, Dad. Look what I found on it last night…"

So much for fatherly advice!

I love the stillness of early morning. I can feel a distinct autumn chill in the air, though it is only early September. Summer flowers still bloom all around the garden and the sun is beginning to warm the patio, but everywhere there are subtle hints that winter is on the way.

My eyes meander around the garden where the boys have grown up. Bereft now of paddling pools and sand-pits, slides and swing-sets, it seems big and empty, left behind from a busier time. Years ago, on long warm evenings after dinner, the boys would entice their father out to play soccer, always squabbling about whose side he should be on.

I can almost hear those high childish voices again – but of course they are gone forever now as the deep bass tones of manhood have taken over. Only the goal posts and the trampoline have been able to bridge the gap between boyhood and adolescence, and even those have hardly been used this past summer. A new world of virtual reality and cyberspace is luring our boys into realms where their father and I cannot follow.

I have been here before, but this time it is different. When Luke started secondary school it was my wake-up call to warn me that my children would not stay little forever, that life was changing. But I could press the snooze button for a while because Tommy was still unmistakeably a child, and even as Luke put away childish things Tommy spread them out again, so I was still surrounded by childhood. But Tommy is the last one – my baby! I can't snooze anymore. I have to get up and begin a new day.

What will that new day hold for me? Will I go back to work? I suppose I might have to if Luke's college plans come to pass! Maybe I'll have time now to take up new hobbies – or even revisit old ones. I can almost feel a tingle of excitement at the thought of rooting out my old paints and brushes again, now that there are no little fingers to meddle in them!

"I'm off, Jenny." John's voice yanks me from my reverie as he plants his good-bye kiss on my lips.

"Ok, see you later," I reply, catching hold of his arm as he turns away. "Did you have a chat with Tommy?"

"Sure, we had a great chat about his new phone over breakfast...."

"Not about the phone, John!" I'm trying to be patient but he's being particularly obtuse. "Haven't you got anything to say to him about school, his first day? Any fatherly advice?"

For a moment he looks baffled, but then I can see the understanding dawn on his face. I feel his arms come around me as tears well up in my eyes.

"He's going to be fine, Jenny," he says softly into my hair. "You have to believe that."

"I know. I do," I insist. "It's just…."

"He's not eight anymore, love. He's a big boy now. He's more able to take care of himself."

"Could you ask Luke to keep an eye on him?" I plead.

"Yes, I already have," he agreed. "But Luke can only do so much. Tommy has to stand on his own feet too. It's a great bonus that he has grown so tall over the summer. He's not going to be an obvious target for bullies. That's a big help."

I know he is right. I have said the same words over and over to myself all summer. But the memory of that awful time when Tommy was bullied is hard to erase. I still remember the weeks of trying to coax him to go to school, not able to understand why a boy who loved school suddenly didn't want to go.

We asked him if anyone was being mean to him, but he kept denying it. We even contacted the school to see if they had noticed anything, but they were in the dark too. It was only when his best friend confided in his own mother that we found out Tommy was being bullied. It took two years of patient encouragement before Tommy loved school again.

But he has moved on. He has put the past behind him and let it go. And somehow I must do the same.

"You're right, he'll be fine," I smile my thanks. "I'm just being silly."

"No, you're just being a mother," he corrects me, reminding me again of why I love him. "But he'll be fine."

We head back inside, his arm still around my shoulders. The boys have finished breakfast, and also their squabbling, it seems, for a while at least.

"We're off too," says Luke cheerfully, swinging his heavy school-bag onto one shoulder with ease. Tommy copies the gesture, staggering slightly under the weight of his.

"It's too early, the bus won't be there yet," I point out, glancing at the clock.

"Dad's dropping us off at school on his way to work," Luke casually informs me. Suddenly the moment is here. There is no time for last minute nerves. I want to delay them, but there is no reason. Everything is organised, lunches are packed and the boys are ready for school.

I look at them standing together, dressed in the same uniform yet so different, on opposite ends of the journey into manhood. They are starting this new season together, but by the end of it, they will be in very different places. For one, this is a season of beginnings; for the other, a season of endings. For me, it's a season of letting go.

"Are you ok?" I ask Tommy, hoping he can't see my nervousness.

"Of course," he answers bravely, innocently thinking I can't see his.

I resist the urge to hug him, frantically sorting through all the advice and cautions in my head for one last word of wisdom that will solve everything ... Try to make friends ... Don't let anyone bully you ... Go find your brother if you have any problems.

Luke turns away, heading towards the front door, but not before I catch him rolling his eyes at his Dad.

"Don't worry, Tom," I say calmly. "You'll be great."

Already I am learning the language of letting go.

The Beginners Short Story Winner

THE LAST CHERRY BLOSSOM

BY KATHRYN BURKE
Clontarf, Dublin

Sigrid had come to Ireland from her native Norway because of the light and her husband, Martin; now he is dead and gone, and soon the light would be gone too ...

LIGHT WANDERED through her house and touched her gently like a benediction. They had bought the house because of the light, taken down walls to give it paths to travel; she had never worried if it revealed an opportunistic cobweb. Light had always been her obsession.

Sigrid no longer shared the light with Martin. *Jeg elsker deg,* she had whispered in her native Norwegian, watching his coffin go into the grave. There had been just the two of them in their thirty-four year marriage. No child, no grandchild, to whom she could now say *I love you.* No blood kin in Ireland. *Jeg elsker deg - I love you.* Redundant now, in Norwegian and English.

She had come from Tromso. Growing up in the darkness of Norway's nocturnal winters, Sigrid vowed to run south as soon as she got out of university, head for Granada, Naples, Tangier, anywhere you could look up at the winter sky and recognise it was day.

Then she had attended a conference in Dublin and noticed how, even in the most depressing November, you had light from nine to five, light that changed from charcoal to pale grey and then to the luminous sheen of a pearl. She had met Martin at one of the seminars. Martin and the Irish light - they had been more than enough.

Just a year after Martin's death, she had noticed the deterioration in her sight. I am going to lose light too, she thought.

But spring had arrived this morning, quietly, without fuss, as it so often did in Ireland. Suddenly there was a softness in the air and the light had new energy, as if it had been to a spa for a course of treatment. At the end of her Dalkey garden a cherry tree unfolded its blossoms.

Sigrid stood at the sitting room window, eating a rye cracker with a slice of the fudge coloured Norwegian cheese that tasted of home, and admired the inviting way the tree raised its white branches to the sky. As if it wished to marry the light, be its bride.

And she could still see it. It had been her reward for getting up.

She had woken that morning from the darkness of sleep and lay, motionless and tense, as she always did now, afraid to open her eyes. In case the darkness, not the visible darkness of an unlit bedroom but something deeper and denser, remained with her.

When, almost against her will, her eyelids flickered, she saw a dot of green, the glow of the handset phone in its cradle. It shone like a traffic light. Go on, it's safe. It gave her the confidence to turn on the bedside lamp and let the pale walls - *Irish Barley* - slide into view. The sweater she had thrown across a chair the night before was sunshine yellow. Colours. They had remained with her.

So she could swing her legs out of bed and pad across the carpet to draw the curtains. And there was the morning light and the blossoming cherry tree, waiting to greet her.

With each day, with the relief of a world brought back into view, she felt she was given a choice, a challenge, one she could not always meet. Resented, more often than not, having to meet. Be positive. Be grateful. On bad days she would grit her teeth and drink too many cups of strong black coffee. Positive about what? Grateful to whom, and for what? Her husband was dead, her sight was going.

But this morning she could see a cherry tree. And her pal Rita, from the verse writing group, out walking her dog. She took him to Mass with her every morning. She was a dumpling of a woman, good-hearted and tactful. Sigrid knew she was lucky to have her as a friend. When things became difficult she'd be the best person to confide in. Not just yet, though.

She seemed to be mouthing something. Sigrid opened the

window. At least her hearing was sharp. "It deserves a haiku," Rita was shouting, "your cherry tree. Doesn't it? Write one for the next meeting." As if to strengthen the statement she opened Sigrid's gate, clomped across the lawn and stood with her dog, a bichon frise, under the cherry tree, her halo of white hair as fine as the alabaster blossom, the cotton wool, short-legged dog the perfect accessory for his owner.

A haiku? Sigrid watched Rita and the bichon frise turn and waddle down the drive. For a moment they seemed trapped inside the sun's rays, like an illustration in a children's book. The wonder of light. Could she write about that tableau - the cherry tree, her friend, the little dog, counting her syllables and counting a good moment in her morning? To remind her that there were still good moments.

Swallowing the end of the cheese and cracker, Sigrid went into the study she had shared with Martin. It was too cluttered. When things got darker she would need more space; she'd have to be able to cross the room easily, not bump into things.

Every day she set herself some tasks, "Find it in the dark" tasks. Now she stood at the desk, closed her eyes, and let her right hand move down to the top handle. Her thumb and first finger curled around its oval shape. She pulled out the drawer and felt inside.

A finger got caught between the sharp edges of a stapler. Careful. She extricated it gingerly then slid her hand until she touched the oblong box of paper clips. Her A4 manuscript book was under it. She lifted the book, closed the drawer and opened her eyes. Task accomplished.

She could wander around her house now at night, without electricity. It had been a training programme which had brought some knocks and bruises. But she needed to get ready for the time when she would live in permanent darkness.

Movements that seemed daunting, like going up the stairs, had been easy enough. She went slowly, feeling each step with her foot, clutching the handrail. She was careful when she touched the newel post, paused before she stepped on to the landing.

It was often absence of mind, the moment when she lost concentration, which created problems. There had been a night when she forgot the bedroom door was ajar, and walked into its edge. Her nose had stung for weeks. Toddy McCarthy, her GP, wasn't complimentary. "You'll break your neck, Mrs. Devlin. For God's sake, have a bit of sense. And talk to someone."

Now, as she remembered the incident and Dr. McCarthy's advice, Sigrid acknowledged that part of her problem lay in her silences. She was a reticent woman.

Martin said she proved what truth there could be in stereotypes, the reserved Scandinavian in her case. It was only with him that words had flown from her. '*Jeg elsker deg, Jeg elsker deg.*' Or sometimes, *Jeg er glad i deg* - Martin had liked that expression, said it had a Gaelic twist to it.

Don't think of Martin now. Think of the haiku. Could she capture the wonder of the newly unfurled cherry tree? It deserved a tribute. Would she be blind to its glory next spring?

Closing her eyes again, she felt the bevelled edge of the desk, then its smooth mahogany surface. Yes, her Parker pen and old-fashioned inkwell were still there. The advantage of being the only person in a house was that no one moved things. She placed the manuscript book beside the pen. Don't open the eyes yet. She was doing well, now she could sit down.

But if no other person moved things in the house, Sigrid sometimes did. She had walked to the desk and stood at it - no chair. Where was it, the sturdy office chair bought in a junk shop in Temple Bar, before the area became trendy? Ah yes, she had pushed it back yesterday when she'd been polishing the woodblock floor, it was against the bookcase.

Don't cheat, Sigrid, keep your eyes closed and find it. She turned and took a step, holding her hands stiffly in front of her; she felt uneasy now, unable to gauge the space. She moved back a step, hitting her hip against the desk. Her elbow swept some objects from its surface. She heard a thud as they fell on the floor, then the staccato sound of breaking glass. Her eyes flew open.

The silver frame, with Martin's photograph, lay face upwards, undamaged. But the inkwell - 18th century, rare, valuable, which he had given her for their tenth anniversary - was in jigsaw shards. A pool of dark blue Waterman's ink moved, like a small flood, towards Martin's face.

Sigrid knelt beside the mess and began to mop at it ineffectually with some tissues from the waste-paper basket. She wished she could cry but the capacity for tears was drying up in her, like her sight.

So what was the point of this foolish positivity? No one can be brave all the time. And, at this moment, she didn't feel brave Husband gone - she'd never find another Martin. And sight? They didn't offer a replacement at *Clancy's - Ophthalmic Opticians.*

Rage against the dying of the light. Wasn't that a line from the Welsh poet, Dylan Thomas, a master of verse. Well, Sigrid was raging. Quite as much as Dylan Thomas would have wished. Because this time next year she might never see a cherry tree again, or this clear, high sky.

"Write a haiku," Rita had said. Easy for her, as she trotted to Mass, still able to find her way with confidence, in spite of enough flesh to make chairs creak when she sat in them. How angry it made Sigrid, the way people would offer these cheery sound bites to the besieged.

Her friends, her attempts at verse, the training programme she had put in place so that the shock of sightlessness, when it came, would be a little lessened, what were they all but a beaver dam against the weight of water from a Niagara Falls?

Ah, there was that stupid chair. Sigrid lifted it over to the desk and eased herself into it. She looked down at the ink. The pool had turned into a lake. It had spread beyond the shadow of the desk, into the sunlight.

She had never known there could be so many mutations, so many shades in Waterman's blue ink. Light transmuted it, turned it azure, shot it with green, made it move and shimmer. The photograph of Martin seemed to float. Alchemy.

Sigrid followed the line of light out through the window, to the greater light beyond. There was the cherry tree. From where she sat, its blossom covered branches seemed to touch the sky, as if its embrace had been accepted. The marriage of tree and light had taken place.

All she had to set against her fear, her rage, was this spring morning. Only this. She wasn't sure it would be enough. But she had seen Rita and her dog caught in a sunbeam, watched an ink pool come alive and touch her husband's face, and a cherry blossom marry the sky. All on this spring morning. So she should capture those moments.

Sigrid opened her manuscript book. How white the paper was. She tested her fountain pen; it had enough ink, for one haiku. Her praise offering to the last cherry blossom. And to the light, and Martin.

And she'd weave in the words:

Jeg elsker deg.
Jeg elsker deg.
Jeg er glad i deg....

Memories Winner

ONCE UPON A HAPPY CHRISTMAS

BY MAE LEONARD

Naas, Co. Kildare

A special treat every Christmas Eve when growing up in Limerick was being brought to the uptown shops by our father, with his favourite bookshop always a highlight

CHRISTMAS EVE was our special day uptown in Limerick with my Dad when he took us shopping. He finished work at midday and my mother had his dinner on the table when he came in. We were dressed in our Christmas best ready for the off.

This particular Christmas Eve Limerick city was bustling with people and we hoped to meet an uncle or two who might slip us a few bob for Christmas. Dad patiently watched and waited while we enjoyed the shop window displays, our faces so close to the glass our breath clouded it.

That was his cue to steer us on to his favourite bookshop – O'Mahony's, O'Connell Street. O'Mahony's was, and still is, an uptown bookshop. On Christmas Eve it smelled of opulence. There were untouchable books with leather binding, large tomes on neat shelves and there was a children's section where my favourite Annuals were on display. Dad allowed us, with a little guidance, to choose a book each.

Then came that year when he eased me away from the children's section and pointed out smaller, more compact books. I read the titles Lorna Doone, Little Women and Black Beauty but somehow they didn't appeal to me.

One particular book with a plain green cloth cover caught my eye. Because it had neither front picture nor illustrations it seemed to call out "Pick me".

Dad was a bit surprised at my choice but, fair play to him, he took it to the counter with my brother's 'Robin Hood' where the books were carefully wrapped in brown paper and tied with twine. The books were Dad's special gift to us.

It was the same Christmas Eve that my Mam decided that I was responsible enough to stay up late and baby-sit my little sister. Then Mam, Dad and my big brother, with his soutane and surplice rolled under his arm, headed out into the frosty night to the parish church for Midnight Mass.

Oh, I felt so important, I was in charge. I had been warned, of course, not to touch anything Mam had set up in the kitchen for the Christmas dinner. The stuffing was ready in the big basin, the turkey cleaned out and a huge sherry trifle stood, still steaming, in Granny's glass bowl.

My little sister was fast asleep in the bedroom just off the kitchen. She and I shared that room and I had permission to stay up as long as I wanted to. I didn't feel at all sleepy.

So I prised open the top cover of the range and put in a few more sods of turf and rattled the damper to liven it up a bit. Then I curled up on Dad's big armchair and opened my brand new book, Knocknagow by Charles Kickham, and underneath the title I read....

You meet him in his cabin rude,
Or dancing with his dark eyed Mary,
You'd swear there was no other mood
But mirth and love in Tipperary.

I thumbed to the first chapter.

"It is Christmas Day. Mr. Henry Lowe has just opened his eyes, and ...

Oh this was bliss.

I think I was on the third page and perhaps my eyelids were drooping a bit when suddenly, in the quiet, I heard the tinkling of bells. Was that the sound of church bells or was it more like Jingle Bells? Jingle Bells? No! Couldn't be, could it? Was that thudding on the roof a reindeer? Was that St. Nicholas sliding down the chimney?

I didn't wait to find out. I ran into the bedroom and dived, fully clothed, into bed with my baby sister, shoved my book under the pillow and pulled the blankets over my head.

I must have fallen asleep. It was still dark when I woke again with a wonderful feeling of peace and calm. I shook my little sister awake and saw that Santa Claus had indeed come and with enforced gusto, together we opened our presents, shivering with excitement or perhaps it was cold?

We pulled a couple of crackers, blew up a couple of balloons and donned paper hats. Suddenly I heard voices. The front door squeaked open. There was somebody coming into our house! The bedroom door swung open. I screamed. My sister screamed. We both screamed together.

"What the...?"

"Dad, dad," my sister cried, "look what Santa brought me."

They stood there, mouths open in astonishment, Mam, Dad and my big brother, all with flakes of snow glistening in their hair, looking like angels, returning from Midnight Mass.

Somehow, sanity was restored and we were soothed back to sleep.

Next time I woke it was in broad daylight to the mouth-watering smells of Happy Christmas cooking. I smiled to myself and reached under my pillow for my book, turned over the pages to the first chapter and began to read again –

"It is Christmas Day. Mr. Henry Lowe has just opened his eyes, and is debating with himself whether it is the grey dawn or only the light of the young moon... "

Open Short Story Runner-Up

NEW SHOE DAY

BY JENNIFER MAY
Sallynoggin, Co. Dublin

Rosie is big for her age and is especially conscious of her feet. The occasional shopping expeditions for new shoes are a source of particular torture ...

MY NEW *Clarks* squeak as I go up the stairs to my bedroom. They are heavy leather, plain with thick unsightly laces and flat wide heels. *Nigger Brown* they call the colour; I hate it. They are like a form of punishment, these shoes, but my mother says I have to wear them because of my more-narrow-than-usual-feet and my longer-than-usual big toe.

Even the friendly lady in the shoe-shop in Dun Laoghaire where we go for fittings, has to turn away her head when she sees the size of my big toe. I know she's laughing at me, but my mum says I'm imagining it. "Your feet look fine Rosie," she says. "They may be a bit on the large size, but then, you are a big girl for your age."

If mum thinks she is making me feel better with that remark she is sorely mistaken. I know I'm big for my age; I live with that knowledge every day. I tower above all the other girls in my class and they never let me forget it either. A big lanky streak of misery, that's me, with my trousers always just a little bit too short and my ankles showing: a lanky streak of misery that's already topping five feet eleven before I'm even twelve.

Underneath mum knows how much it hurts not to be able to wear pretty delicate footwear in a variety of eye-catching colours, like other girls my age, because when we're finished, and the shoes are laced-up tight on my miserable feet, she takes me for a cup of tea and a sticky bun in the Kylemore Café.

When we're sitting down, she takes my hand across the table and tells me that my shoe ordeal - the wearing of shoes with special narrow fittings - will soon be over.

"In another year or two, you'll be able to get normal shoes," she smiles. She looks really pretty sitting across from me with her black hair all done up in an Ava Gardner bun, a touch of eye-liner showing the darkness of her brown eyes. "But your father is right, it's important to have the proper fitting shoes when your feet are growing."

"None of the other girls parents force them to wear special shoes," I say, the same thing I say every year on New Shoe Day. "How come it's only me that has to go around looking like an eejit?"

"Then those girls don't have parents who care about their feet," my mother replies archly, the same thing she says every year on New Shoe Day. The two of us burst out laughing, despite the misery of the occasion.

My father's obsessed with fallen arches. He goes on and on about some dancer named Cyd Charisse and how she had wonderful legs, the best in Hollywood, according to him. She was so light on her feet, he says, lighter than Ginger even, and it was all thanks to the sensible shoes her parents made her wear. My mother laughs uproariously when he says this, the two of them sharing some private joke at my expense, I think.

"Cyd Charisse had polio as a child," my mother finally admits to me when I ask her what was so special about some old hoofer. "She battled against all the odds to become such a wonderful dancer. So, really, Rosie, your father has a point; wearing the right shoes can affect every part of you, especially your posture."

Posture is a big thing in our house; if you are not standing up straight backed and proud, you may as well be dead in my father's eyes. I know in my heart of hearts if it was left to her, my mother would let me wear any shoes I like. She doesn't get much choice in the matter because it is my father who pays the bills; it is him who makes all the decisions.

"Your father is not frivolous by nature, nor does he..." says my mother trying to be fair to him, "...understand the desires of a young girl on the cusp of womanhood."

That statement makes us laugh again, so much so that I spit

tea all over the Formica tabletop, and earn the disapproving glares of a group of old women huddled together in a booth (like the Macbeth witches, says my mother, hubble, bubble toil and trouble). I get a cloth from the lady behind the counter and wipe up the mess, carefully, feeling that my every move is being watched, which makes me self-conscious. I can feel myself blush.

When I sit down and drain my teacup, my mother smiles at me. "You know Rosie, you are a hundred times more beautiful than you realise," she says, and then looks away from me and out the window at the busy main-street, her eyes glittering strangely. She stays silent until we leave.

It is raining. The train is packed with children and their mothers. There is a smell of unwashed gabardine and wet wool. Many of passengers have packages; the week before school starts everyone goes shopping for new clothes. Because the train is so busy, I have to stand in the aisle so I stare down, down at the other passengers' feet. Many of the kids have new shoes on, and there is a variety of styles on show; none of them heavy clodhoppers like mine.

One girl about my age, with blond curls and a fake fur jacket like Alvin Stardust's, keeps glancing down at my feet and then slyly towards her own. I can't stop my eyes from following hers. Her feet are small and shod in little red sandals with strings that tie around her ankles and a little, delicate heel. I look away and imagine myself pulling each curl one-by-one from her ugly head. I stand one foot over the other so no one can see my shoes. I can't wait for my stop. I hate my life.

"Rosie, show us your new shoes. Ahh, they're lovely," my big brother Simon laughs as he aims a punch at me, giving me a dead arm. I push past him, trying to think of a suitably clever riposte - trying to think what my new found hero, Scout Finch, would say - but nothing comes.

"Piss off spotty" I hiss instead, repairing to my bedroom, slamming the door behind me. I delve under the bed for this week's *Jinty* comic. I"ve saved it for three days without even opening it. It nearly killed me, showing such restraint, because that brilliant serialised story, *Fran of the Floods*, is finally coming to its gripping conclusion.

Fran's plight has affected me deeply. I feel like I have been on every step of her journey, although unlike Fran I have never travelled, except Sunday trips to look at the planes taking off from Dublin airport and a week in a tent on a long, wet and windswept beach in the Kerry Gaeltacht.

I kick off my new shoes, which had already started to give me a blister, lie down on my bed wrapping my turquoise (Satin sheen) eiderdown around me. The room is freezing. The bedrooms have old fire-places, but my granddad blocked them up years ago. He believed one, that a fire in a bedroom was dangerous, and two, that cold air was a natural stimulant, good for both the circulation and the brain.

My father had clearly been influenced by memories of his own frosty childhood, because if you complain about the cold he looks at you as if you're mad and tells you to put on another jumper.

Because of this I suppose, my mum spends her evenings knitting jumpers. But she is as terrible a knitter as she is a dressmaker, so the garments she finally casts off, sews up and then expects you to wear, are - like my shoes - a nail in the coffin of my popularity.

Other crosses I bear are my father's old age - everyone thinks he is my granddad; his chronic atheism, which makes the nuns single me out for cruel and unusual punishment, and the alfalfa my mum puts in my lunchbox. All are guaranteed to leave me friendless.

Crooked seams and dropped stitches are the order of the day when my mum knits. Tensions vary so much that one side of the garment may reach the waist, while the other side comfortably covers the knee. Mum insists on both Simon and I wearing her creations. She even knitted his grey school jumper. The yellow and purple stripes around the neckline were all over the place; I almost felt sorry for him wearing that monstrosity into school.

I read the whole comic, keeping *Fran of the Floods* for last. My parents loathe comics. My father calls them imbecilic. I have never seen him laugh as much as when he read *The Courage of Crippled Clara,* a classic *Jinty* tale. Each tear of mirth made me feel intellectually inferior to the rest of my family. I had quite liked it really.

Finally I read *Fran of the Floods*, and it's a massive disappointment, with no satisfying conclusion. I feel cheated. Maybe my father is right when he says that good literature never lets you down. I toss the comic into the bin and pick up "*To Kill a Mockingbird*" instead. Out of the corner of my eye, I can see my new shoes glaring at me from the corner of the room and not for the first time, I wish Atticus Finch was my father.

He wouldn't care what I wore on my feet.

After dinner (sausages, mash and fried onions because it's Wednesday and we always have that on Wednesdays), my father demands to see my new shoes, so I go upstairs reluctantly and put them on. I clomp back down and into the living room, where he is sitting near the fire in his armchair, listening to classical music.

"Walk up and down Rosalie, so I can see if they fit you properly," my father says. I do as he says. My father nods his head in approval.

"What size now?"

He feels the front of the shoes to make sure there is ample "growing room" for my toes. I can see Simon grinning. He's going to tease me later.

"Does it really matter dad?"

"Yes it does Rosalie, I like to keep a record of these things, check that all your development is happening as it should."

"Six," I glare at Simon. Sometimes I wonder if my dad is right in the head. I mean, when I start developing, as he calls it, in other places, is he going to want to measure me there too?

"Six". He shakes his head; "Big feet for an eleven-year-old girl."

"Nearly twelve, I'm nearly twelve," I shout, my eyes brimming with tears of humiliation. I can hear my mother giving out to my father as I flounce out of the sitting room and sit on the stairs. The third step, my sulking step, Simon calls it.

"You never think before you speak, Francis." There is a note of exasperation in her voice. "You know she's sensitive about her size. Do you never think of what it's like to be a young girl of her age?"

"Can you never put yourself in Rosie's shoes?"

There's a short silence and then it dawns on them all what my mother has just said. Even me in my sulk on the stairs, sees the funny side.

Even I allow myself a smile.

Memories Runner-Up

Sugar, Tae and Doris Day

By Vincent J. Doherty
Palmer's Green, London

In the early 1950s the 'picture house' was central to the lives of a great many people, and with post war rationing still in force so was the necessity in the Border areas to smuggle even the essentials of life

BY THE END of the 1950s everybody in our border town of Strabane should have had an encyclopaedic knowledge of films and film stars. This kind of knowledge was as much to do with smuggling sugar and tae as with Doris Day, for in those years after the Second World War, shortages and rationing of the essentials were a way of life in the Six Counties.

Before the Troubles and the boys from Brussels did away with the Customs checks, the innocent transport of such necessities from one side of the Border to the other was an important part of our daily lives for most of us. If it hadn't been for smuggling we wouldn't have enjoyed half as many films, or 'pictures' as we called them in those fondly remembered times.

Going across the Border to Lifford wasn't just about smuggling, it was also about entertainment in the days before wall-to-wall television. For a young boy of my age it was an opportunity to exchange the grey realities of every day life for the technicoloured dreams of the far away world of the 'pictures'.

Regardless of the elements or anything else, we would troop the mile or so across the border for the 'First House' at seven and when we came back two or three hours later with the week's provisions, the customs post would usually be shut and we could have brought a mountain of butter, a sea of tae and a warehouse of sugar for all the customs seemed to care.

We could have set our watches, if we'd had any, by Albert Sturrock, the regular 'Customs Man' whose duty was done by nine when he would haul the very official looking 'Customs' sign inside, lock up for the night and ride off home on a bicycle to his supper, sometimes with his own provisions from 'never mind where' in his saddlebag.

At about the same time Randolph Scott or some other hero would have galloped off across the silver screen and us smugglers would be standing for 'The Soldier's Song' in the picture house before making for home, laden with our contraband and inspired by our dreams.

For the price of two pounds of sugar we could see everything and learn everything that mattered in that palace of dreams, from 'War and Peace' to Bugs Bunny, from 'Quo Vadis' to 'The Eddie Cantor Story' and Mario Lanza, 'The Student Prince', would sing to us.

We could fall in love with Doris Day as 'Calamity Jane' singing amongst the 'Black Hills of Dakota', hills that looked far more impressive than the Sperrins. We could follow Bob Hope and Bing Crosby with Dorothy Lamour on the 'Road' to everywhere, and laugh at The Three Stooges doing their best to brain one another, or Laurel and Hardy tootling on their way, wrecking and wreaking destruction at whatever they turned their hands to.

We could hop on a trolley with Judy Garland and meet Kitty O'Brien at the World's Fair in St. Louis, which appeared to be a far more entertaining fair than Fair Day in Strabane. And the night became 'High Noon' as we walked tall with Gary Cooper.

The smuggling, of course, was not always without its hazards, particularly when there was a zealous 'Relief Customs Man' on duty or it was a night when they were 'stepping up security'. At times like that somebody would give us the nod and concealment of groceries or whatever was the order of the day under as many items of clothing as you'd care to mention, and some you wouldn't care to mention.

Unfortunately such concealments weren't always without their hazards and many's the dozen eggs arrived home already scrambled and many's the pound of body-heated butter arrived home as a ready-made lotion.

It wasn't just groceries that were smuggled. New clothes were hard to get hold of in those days of 'coupons' and the worst loser that I ever heard of was a man called Mulhern. He successfully ordered a new suit from Frank Dooher, whose draper's shop backed on to the River Foyle on the Lifford side.

Mulhern went for a final fitting, tried the suit on and having satisfied himself that it was grand he was so proud of it that he decided to wear it going home through the Customs. Without thinking, he threw his old one out of the window into the river. It was only when he put his hand in his pocket to pay for the new one that he realised he'd left his money in the pocket of the old one and that was now half way to Derry in the fast flowing Foyle.

Beginners Short Story Runner-Up

PERMISSION GRANTED

BY ANNE WALSH DONNELLY
Castlebar, Co. Mayo

Mick and his teenage daughter Tara have been together since the death of Joan eight years earlier, and now Mick has established a relationship with Eileen

"WHERE ARE we going?" It's not the words, more the way Eileen says them. The May sun that only minutes before hinted of a warm summer that might come this year, hides behind a thunderhead.

"Where we always go."

"I don't mean that."

"That's an awful looking cloud over there. We'd better hurry up."

We do our usual loop around the park in silence and even though we walk a lot quicker than usual it seems to take twice as long. Of course I know what she means. Her love infuses my brittle bones and softens stiff muscles. It's great to be loved again. But to be honest I'm happy with the way things are. In my mind we don't need to go anywhere, let alone have a conversation about where we might be going.

"We could go to Pontoon for the weekend if you like. It's about time I brought you and the house is free at the moment," I say.

"We could."

"Great. That's settled then."

She keeps walking in silence, but at least she's still walking with me rather than away. I touch her fingertips with mine and they intertwine albeit temporarily.

I'll never forget the day I met her. I'm not really one to believe in fate or destiny or that sort of stuff but there was some synchronicity going on that morning.

"I'm collecting for the Marie Keating Foundation," she'd said.

I leaned towards her so I could decipher her soft words amidst the ones Lady Gaga was sending down the stairs.

"Not today of all days," I said, thinking of Joan's anniversary mass that was on later.

She turned to walk away.

"Sorry, I didn't mean to be rude. My head's a bit wrecked. Teenagers," I said, nodding towards the stairs.

"I have three, myself; boys. All grown up now," she said. "And you?"

"Just the one, a girl, Tara."

The clouds that had been hanging in the sky all morning burst.

"Come in for a minute, until it lets up. That is...if you don't mind being deafened," I said.

"I'm well used to it."

That was it. Soon we slipped into Saturday nights for dinner and whatever might come after. It was enough for both of us, or so I thought.

"Myself and Eileen are going to Pontoon at the weekend," I tell Tara, when I get home.

As usual she doesn't raise her head from her laptop.

"Well...if the weather's good. Did you hear me?" I say, interrupting her zombie gaze at the laptop screen with a waving hand.

"Yeah....whatever."

Maybe she's just delighted to get a break from my shouts when the volume on her iPod speakers rises. She types furiously; posting her Dad-free weekend status on Facebook, no doubt. I don't know why I worry so much about her.

She was in a funny mood yesterday after she came back from an obligatory two day retreat for her leaving certificate class.

"We never say 'I love you,' Dad."

"But, sure you know I do....Don't you?"

"It would be nice to hear you say it, now and then. Before

Mam died, you used to, every night after my bedtime story."

"Would it stop the arguments now, if I did say it?" I say with a half-laugh.

"Ah...Dad!"

A child creeps back into her teenage voice and I instantly regret my watery joke.

Fathers love their daughters as daughters love their fathers. It's a given, isn't it? Lately it seems that ours is buried deep in arguments over skirts too short and unsuitable boyfriends. I don't see love in the eyes that peer out between the hairs of her brown fringe. Her baby curls cowed by a hair straightener bristle with anger. Anger for not telling her I love her? Is that it? Is that what I should do?

I can't remember what I told Tara on the day of Joan's funeral. All I can remember is a little girl sitting in a Barbie pop up tent in her bedroom, the one we had bought for her seventh birthday. I tried to coax her downstairs to play with her cousins and have something to eat. Instead she ate sandwiches and drank Coke in her tent. Later, as I hoovered the crumbs, the half-eaten sandwiches left behind, I cried for our loss - the only time I cried.

I knock on her bedroom door, on my way to bed.

"Yeah?"

She hides her mobile phone under the pillow as I enter. I stop myself from launching into a rant and sit on the edge of her bed.

"I do. Love you."

She throws her arms around me and part of me wishes that I could read her a bedtime story now.

The rest of the week flies by. I had been looking forward and dreading the weekend in equal measure, but standing against the heat of the wood burning stove, it feels good to be home. The smell of the wood dispels the musty odour of a sporadically inhabited house. Two half cups of lukewarm tea stand beside an opened packet of custard creams on the kitchen table.

Wood creaks upstairs as Eileen opens drawers. My back aches

from chopping wood and carrying her case. I had forgotten how much stuff a woman packs, even if it's only for the weekend.

I go outside to bring in more wood before the sun recedes. There's no teenage music to wreck my head. It's so quiet that I can hear the water lick the walls of the small pier at the bottom of the garden. The smells of the lake air and sap from chopped timber remind me of why I still visit.

The hinge on the timber gate that separates garden from lake has been fixed since I was here last. What would I do without my brother? He tries so hard to keep our childhood home alive, lighting fires to dispel dampness and meeting the German fishermen who occasionally rent the house. I put the excess wood into the shell of the black Morris Minor that guards the gate to Mam's orchard where branches still droop with apples in September.

As I come back into the kitchen, the electric shower starts upstairs. The sound of the pump groaning as it churns out water startles me. I picture the stream pouring over Eileen's body as she washes away the journey's grime. Then I flinch as a blue bottle fly brushes against my cheek and guilt hits me. Was it right to bring her here? Is it right to steal from her bed on Saturday nights, to go from lover to father at two in the morning? It was easy at first and she understood. I needed to collect Tara from the nightclub. There didn't have to be awkward conversations about staying the night. We've known each other physically for a year and now she wants to break my emotional hymen and I'm scared.

"That smells good," Eileen says, as she comes into the kitchen.

She has a knack for saying the right words at the right time. The velvet tone in her voice drapes around my frazzled head. God, I'd really miss her voice.

"Re-heating's my speciality."

In the midst of light from tea candles on the table and the half-moon's rays in the night sky, she could be twenty two instead of fifty two. Fronds of dark hair dampen the collar of her cream blouse. The vision in front of me is more tempting than the Marks and Spencer dinner in the oven and the smell of her newly-soaped body more appetising.

She chats incessantly as we eat. My em's and ah's are timed impeccably and keep the conversation moving. The moon's light is too sharp now so I close the blind as shadows dance over the lake's black surface in the same way as I've let my heart dance on the surface of love.

"Is there any salt," she asks.

Thankfully there's a container of Saxa in the press that the last group of fishermen must have left behind. I bang it off the worktop to loosen the granules. She sprinkles it liberally over the poached salmon.

"There's probably enough salt on that already."

She stops sprinkling and looks at the window's closed blind for a moment, then turns her head as if she is about to say something, but doesn't.

"Sorry, Eileen. Tara's a terror for loading salt on her dinner."

"I see."

Her stern tone tells me she doesn't see at all. It tells me in no uncertain terms that I'm eating with an adult not a child or teenager. We finish our meal, clear the table, wash and dry plates, glasses and cutlery in silence. Not the easy silence of a middle aged couple who have lived half a lifetime together with the minimum of words passing between them and are now oblivious to each other's idiosyncrasies. No - we're in a virginal silence that needs to be broken if we are to survive the weekend. Only I don't know if I can.

"I left my make-up bag in the car."

"I'll get it."

"No, stay – I need some fresh air anyway."

The door creeps shut after her and the woody air tries to sedate me. My eyelids droop and I remember what Tara had said to me, eight summers ago in this kitchen.

"I don't want you to ever get another wife, I don't want another Mammy."

Is that the hook I'm hanging onto now? Or is it the fear of loving and losing again? I don't want another doctor telling me a woman I love has only weeks to live.

The heat that was in the kitchen earlier has left. I open the stove to stoke up the embers. Acrid smoke escapes and fills my lungs. I cough and can't stop. My eyes sting and start to water. I bang the stove door shut and lean against the worktop, coughing, spluttering and dribbling.

The latch on the back door squeaks and I feel Eileen's eyes run over me as she walks past. She sits at the kitchen table and waits. Somehow I manage to pull myself together. I wonder if her usual equanimity has helped. I turn towards her. She's folding a sodden tissue in her hands meticulously in ever smaller squares as she looks at me. It's a look I haven't seen before. I search her face for reassurance.

"Maybe I want more than you can give," she says.

Silence descends once more. Then my phone beeps and jumps on the worktop. Eileen gets to it first and hands it to me.

"Tara?"

"Yes. I didn't think I'd hear from her all weekend. She's always too busy with her own stuff nowadays."

"They grow up so fast. We only have them on loan. That's what the boys' Dad used to say to me when they were younger. We need to have our own lives too."

"Yeah, if they'd let us..."

"...or if we'd let ourselves, Mick."

I turn away to read the text.

Enjoy ure weekend dad u cud do worse luv T

Whatever's stopping me, it's not Tara. The candles on the table flicker. I could let them die and be on my own again. Instead I open the drawer, get some more and light them to keep the darkness away. Eileen sits at the table waiting. I step into her circle of heat. It warms me more than the stove or the flames from the candles can. I kneel down and put my arms around her thin waist.

"Tara will probably be going to college in September. I've always wanted to move back here. Would you come ... with me?"

"I love you too," she says, hugging me tightly.

Open Short Story Short Runner up

A Mere Bagatelle

By Tony McGettigan
Dun Emer Drive, Dublin

John had been going out with Julie regularly for two months and had imagined he knew her. He was thinking, music is so important to me, such an important part of my life, how could I have missed Julie's lack of interest in it?

"YOU DON'T like 'Für Elise'!" John repeated.

"Is that what it's called?" Julie replied.

Her indifference surprised him. He thought, 'it isn't important', but he felt something significant had happened. They were having after-dinner coffee in the expensive restaurant with an impressive view of the bay. A lovely summer day was fading. The sky was a wispy pink. A soft, end-of-day half-light filled the room with drowsy torpor.

John and Julie were at the window table. John had asked specifically for it, when he had booked. Waves splintered in cascades of foam on the rocks below the window. Sometimes you could hear their breaking as a distant murmur that was somehow soothing.

They were an attractive couple. He was tall and athletic with a strong face and silvery hair conveying confidence and experience. She was very feminine. Her lively, expressive face was framed by dark, wavy hair. He was noticeably older but it did not seem to matter. Everyone thought them an attractive couple.

The only other customers, clinging to the remains of the evening, were two women in smart business suits, leaning towards each other in earnest conversation, and two young lovers touching finger-tips. There were discreet distances between the tables. One had to listen carefully to hear the piped music. It was that kind of restaurant.

John had been going out with Julie regularly for two months

and had imagined he knew her. He was thinking, music is so important to me, such an important part of my life, how could I have missed Julie's lack of interest in it?

"But it's such a lovely tune," he said and lah, lahed it softly.

"Yes?" Julie replied, using the affirmative as a question, and continued, "I know it but I don't like it."

"Where have you heard it?"

"It seems to be on every phone hold that doesn't have 'Greensleeves'."

"Really?" That's not so. Really?"

Because he was upset by the unexpected disruption of the usual pleasant empathy between them, he felt it necessary to show that he was not upset. He casually picked-up his coffee cup and held it between his finger-tips, turning it slowly, carefully, anticlockwise. The cup was empty. A series of ring stains marked its gradual emptying. He stopped turning it and cupped it in his hands with one thumb through its handle, as if being particularly careful not to spill its contents. He pretended to drink from it, holding it in both hands. Then he replaced it carefully in its saucer.

"It's Beethoven," he said, looking directly at her.

"From the film?" she asked, with a hint of flirtatiousness.

When he did not respond, she added "That's a joke," but she stopped smiling.

"I never met anyone who didn't like 'Für Elise'."

"I don't know it really. But I have heard of Beethoven. I was only joking about the film. You know, the film about the dog, a big, floppy dog; Saint Brendans I think they're called? There were a few of them, the "Beethoven" films."

"No."

"By the way, that's another joke. I know they're Saint Bernards, not Saint Brendans."

John did not reply. He was thinking of music as a metaphor for love.

"It's an age thing I think," Julie continued. "As you get older, undue regard for the classical replaces undue regard for the popular."

John felt there was an implication that the statement applied only to him, not to her; that she had not yet reached that state, had not yet had that inflexibility grow on her.

He looked out the window, away across the bay. The last sailboats were making for harbour. They seemed lost and lonely, ploughing lonely furrows, as he was. It was hard to imagine real people on them, lively, active people, purposefully working ropes and tillers and things, heading happily for harbour.

Some of the greyness, the flatness, the emptiness, of the twilight scene entered his soul. He felt...old. Well, he was old. Was he? He was sixty, but Julie had allowed him to forget it. She was . . . he didn't know her age. It didn't matter to him. Both of them had been on their own for many years, trying to find space in their hearts for someone to replace - no, not to replace, that would be impossible - someone to fit beside the loved one that had been lost.

Then they had met, nothing planned, not even sought, well, maybe, perhaps subconsciously. Who's to say how, why, things happen; who can sense the undercurrent of fate even when caught in it, even when tossed up by it on another shore?

"A penny for your thoughts," Julie said softly.

Avoiding his thoughts, John said, "I don't know how anyone could dislike 'Für Elise.' It's so beautiful."

"I don't really know it. But I have heard of Beethoven. I was only joking about the film, you know, the "Beethoven" films, about the dog."

She spoke gently, sensing that something had slipped from its accustomed place. She raised an eyebrow quizzically and John was suddenly sharply aware of her beauty. He had not felt like that about anyone, since his loss. He felt lucky to be experiencing it again, that glorious feeling that defied definition. Feeling it so sharply and knowing it to be so ephemeral made him want to cry.

He said, "You look lovely."

She smiled, looking at him but somehow smiling to herself. What was she thinking? Was she pleased or embarrassed that he had said what he had said, that he thought of her that way?

Was he making a fool of himself? Was he being ridiculous? She did not acknowledge his compliment. Maybe she had heard it so many times that it meant nothing to her anymore. But "lovely" was not a word John used carelessly.

"I'd say you were a handsome man, when you were young," she said. "Well, I mean you still are, handsome, distinguished looking."

It sounded condescending. Was he being over-sensitive?

"Thanks. When you spend a lot of time on your own, you need a bit of flattery now and again, some reassurance." He hoped he sounded lightly humorous.

"Tell me about it," she said.

Was she referring to herself? Surely someone as beautiful and attractive as she was did not need reassurance. But, maybe we all need reassurance; maybe we are all insecure, in our innermost, private selves, our insecurity a fundamental part of our human nature, our fallen state, our exile from Paradise that left us isolated in an alien world.

"It's been a lovely evening, thanks," Julie said. "I haven't been here before, it's a beautiful place, I've really enjoyed it."

She excused herself and went to the "Ladies". John paid the bill. He felt almost underhand about paying. How, he wondered, could paying for someone's meal be an issue? But he knew that it was, for some, that for some, in a world different to the one he had grown up in, it had connotations he did not understand. When Julie returned, he would tell her casually that he had paid the bill and he hoped she would not say, "Oh, you shouldn't have!" A refusal now to accept graciously such a slight show of friendship would be too much.

He turned to the window and looked out to sea. It was dark, deep dark, nothing solid or definite could be seen in that world of shapes and shades. The room and his face were reflected in the window. He looked unseeingly. The outside blackness was made even blacker by the intermittent flash of a lighthouse somewhere near the restaurant; it's sweeping pencil of light revealed wrinkled waves rolling to eternity.

He counted the seconds between the flashes. When he knew

the pattern, he tried to anticipate the flashes. Sometimes he did. In the distance, on the other side of the bay, another lighthouse pricked the darkness. To those at sea, the lighthouses were welcoming signs of harbour and home but John felt them as symbols of isolation and something drained from his soul.

Why had he felt that Julie could fill, would fill, would ease, his emptiness? It was a mistake to have had optimistic expectations. There was no foundation for them. It was only he who had had expectations. He had taken all the initiatives; Julie had merely gone along with them. That's all there was to it. His loneliness had disposed him to believe . . . had led him to hope . . . implanted expectations that were not justified.

In the reflection in the window, he saw Julie coming towards him across the room, picking her way between the tables. The two young lovers were engrossed in each other and paid no attention to Julie. The two business women looked up as she passed and then looked after her, towards him, and seemed to examine him for a second. He turned from the dark window and smiled at her as she approached.

"It's much later than I thought," he said. "We should be getting along."

"Yes, I can't believe it. The evening flew." She looked into the darkness outside. "The lighthouse creates such a lonely feeling," she said.

He did not mention the bill, neither did she.

In the car park, she exclaimed, "Oh, look!" and pointed at the large moon laying a path of light across the bay. He put his arm around her waist and pulled her to him gently. She did not resist, nor reciprocate. They stood like that for awhile, looking along the path of the moon. But he felt removed from it all. He felt he was floating above them, gazing down on their close separateness.

He drove to her place in a patter of pleasant small talk. Her apartment was in a quiet, leafy street. A neighbour's dog was barking at the full moon. She did not invite him in. It was late. Too late, he said to himself. In the parked car, she turned towards him. Her breast touched his arm as she faced him. She laid her hand gently on his hand on the gear stick and kissed him on the cheek. When he turned towards her, she had already turned away and was searching for the door handle.

"It's below the small light," he said.

She opened the door and got out. The door closed with a decisive clunk. The softness of her kiss lingered on his cheek.

She walked around to his side of the car and signalled to him to lower the window. When he lowered it, he noticed that the dog had stopped barking. The night air was cold. Julie leaned into the car a little, one hand on the door, the other on the roof. Was she going to kiss him, on the lips; was she going to . . .?

"Für Elise," she said, "You know," and lah, lahed the opening bars, "Is it a symphony?"

"No, no, it's a bagatelle, that's all, a mere bagatelle."

"Oh!"

She said "Goodnight" cheerfully and turned away from him and walked quickly into the darkness of her empty apartment. He watched her disappear. A faint light came on behind heavy curtains. He pulled away from the kerb. He did not switch on the radio. He drove slowly in silence. The roads were deserted. When he arrived at his house, it was locked tight, dark and empty, untouched by anything since he had left it earlier that night.

Memories Runner Up

Forty Winks

By Fergus Caulfield

Canvey Island, Essex

An army bandsman recalls the day Russian leader Boris Yeltsin was to be given a civic welcome by the Irish Taoiseach when he touched down at Shannon airport

AS A BANDSMAN in the army I performed at a variety of concerts and functions, everything from village fetes in front of sheep, to political summits in front of world leaders. A day I will never forget was the 30th of September 1994, when Boris Yeltsin, the then president of Russia, would stop over at Shannon airport to meet the Irish Taoiseach (Prime Minister), Albert Reynolds.

Having been in the band for a few years I knew that the more important the dignitary and occasion, the longer we would be on parade. In the case of Boris, it was waiting to beat all waiting.

After a two hour bus journey we arrived at Shannon airport, rendezvousing with the battalion of soldiers providing the guard of honour for inspection. Another hour later we marched into position and stood at ease alongside the runway, knowing from previous experience we had a long wait yet.

Within minutes I was starting to feel the cold, my thin shirt and tunic provided little protection against the freezing wind that can only be experienced at an Irish airport.

You could be enjoying warm sunshine five minutes away from any airport in Ireland, even outside the front door of the terminal, but as soon as you stepped onto the tarmac near the runway, the temperature would drop by at least ten degrees and the wind would increase by the same rate of knots.

My half fingered gloves gave some warmth to my hands, but the tips of my fingers slowly started to become numb, pinker than a new-born piglet, sticking to the metal keys of the clarinet when I tried to play.

After an hour or so the Taoiseach arrived. This was a good sign; we couldn't be much longer, surely? They wouldn't have the poor fellow standing out in the cold unless Boris's arrival was imminent?

After playing the Irish national anthem we stood to ease again, waiting for Boris and his plane to land. The anticipation that I was over half way through my ordeal provided me with some psychological respite... briefly.

My back was aching and my nose ran like a broken tap. I shivered and swore. My right leg had a life of its own, shaking away like an Elvis Presley dance routine, until finally a civil servant appeared, slithering over to the Taoiseach, whispering into his ear. All I can remember about him was that he wore a lovely big thick warm overcoat. It wasn't a long conversation and Mr Reynolds spun round and climbed back into his big black State car, disappearing back to the terminal.

"What the hell is going on," I said to myself, "This is taking the mick"

You might presume that we too were able to disappear into the warmth, but no such luck. We were on parade and would stay there – probably for ever. Two soldiers from the guard of honour fainted flat onto their faces, a fairly drastic way of getting out of there. Another painful freezing hour passed until the Taoiseach reappeared in his Jaguar. When his chauffeur opened his car door I swear I felt the heat from within.

The officer in charge ordered us to attention - Boris's giant jet had arrived, taxiing to a halt a hundred feet from us. The red carpet was rolled out as the airplane door opened and the steps were lowered to the tarmac.

"Thank good God," I said shivering like I was being electrocuted, "Let's get on with it."

An air hostess stuck her head out from the doorway and quickly went back inside, probably amazed that she had landed in a country colder than Russia.

Ten minutes later a few men walked down the steps of the plane; none of whom were Yeltsin.

Albert escorted them to the guard of honour, the officer

saluting them as we played the Russian national anthem.

I could clearly see the foreign diplomats now and Boris definitely wasn't amongst them. Just before I was sure I would collapse with frostbite, or was frozen forever as a human musical statue, we marched off.

I could just about lift my legs, my hands were numb and I had given up trying to sniff my runny nose. I wasn't looking forward to thawing out; the pain would increase as the circulation and warmth gradually returned to my extremities.

Finally, three hours after parading, we were dismissed, clambering as best we could to the solitary tea urn in the corner of the hanger for some sustenance. As we sat quietly on the journey home RTE news relayed the tale of how Boris was a "bit sleepy" and couldn't get off the plane.

As for me, well I was just glad to be on the way home to Cork, my city by the Lee.

Beginners Short Story Runner-Up

A Mother's Blessing

By Anne McCormack

Enniscorthy, Co. Wexford

Childhood sweethearts, Martin and Mary, had made the hard decision to leave for America, against the wishes of Mary's mother. The neighbours were gathering for the farewell 'wake'

IT WAS A DAY like all the other days in March. The mountain road was bleak, grass trodden down by weeks of rain. There seemed to be no let-up this year. Looking back now, on that March day in 1912, it had been a strange day all told. The morning was clear with a watery sun, rain clouds hung in the sky towards the horizon. They made the prospect of rain imminent, if not before noon, certainly by evening.

A feeling of sadness gripped the people gathering on the road outside the cottage. They had come for the 'American Wake', a term given to a farewell party when someone was emigrating from rural Ireland in olden days. Some of the group were huddled together, talking quietly, taking shelter from the rain. One or two had their eyes fixed on the horizon keeping watch for the young couple.

It was now close to six o'clock, the sky already inky black with a biting March wind blowing up the valley. Brandy seemed lame when he came into view. As the dog came closer you could see he was wet, dirty and visibly distressed. Having circled the house a few times whimpering, he took off again up the narrow road that wound its way towards the bog.

Somebody said, "That's Brandy, Mary's dog, where are they? Something is not right." A terrible feeling of foreboding descended on the group.

Martin had called for Mary at noon that day in March.

"Mary come with me, I'm going to the bog for turf in the small creel basket. It can be our way of seeing the bog for one last time. I promised my folks I would meet them in your house for the farewell 'do' this evening."

"All right, I need to talk to you before this evening."

Mrs. Boyle wondered what Mary had in mind. How could her daughter be so selfish? "I hope Mary does the right thing," she thought. "Take care, you two up there," she said as they left.

"Oh Mam, we have been to the bog many times, of course we'll be fine."

Mrs. Boyle watched them walk hand in hand up the narrow road, brandy as always yapping at her daughter's heels. The woman had mixed feelings about the young man who was so taken with her only child. Martin and Mary had been school friends, a friendship that had developed into something more over the years.

Mary was seven years old when she and her mother returned to Barna to live with an elderly aunt. Nothing much was said at the time about Mary's father. There had been talk of an incident with a young girl, but mountain people are good at keeping secrets and in time the talk died down.

Life was hard for single women in rural Ireland at the turn of the century. The Boyles kept a few chickens and ducks as did most of their neighbours. They also owned a section of bog where turf was cut for the winter months. The women made some extra money by lace making, doing crochet, knitting and sprigging. Deliveries were made by horse and cart from a centre in Carndonagh. Agents in Derry and Belfast bought the craft work.

Mrs. Boyle also laid out the dead for the local undertaker down in Milltown. She had been bringing Mary with her recently to 'learn the trade'. Mary was uneasy working with the dead, she dreamed of escaping this life in the mountains and travelling abroad. Martin had provided the answer.

Martin's family lived in Milltown. His father did occasional work on the local large farm owned by the Morton family. He and Martin had also been to the hiring fairs or 'rabbles' in Letterkenny and Derry to offer their labour. The two men had worked in Scotland on occasions picking potatoes. The 'tatie hokers', the Scottish people called this invasion from Ireland each year. Martin had hopes and dreams of a better life away from Milltown. He had two brothers in America and this was his big chance to join them.

Mrs. Boyle was angry that Martin seemed to have persuaded Mary to go with him to America. Mary was torn between her mother and the boy she loved. If she left she would most probably never see her mother again. However, she felt that if she was to stay she would be buried alive here and Martin would be gone forever. Could Mary be happy living the life her mother wanted for her?

"You are only nineteen, you will find someone else."

"No Mam, I will never find anyone like Martin. I love him, don't you understand?"

"If you go, you go without my blessing. You will kill me. I won't ever see you again, I cannot live that long."

"Mam don't say that."

"Even if you don't meet another boy Mary, there is a very good and kind matchmaker in Killybegs."

"Mam that's awful, what would Dad say if he heard you talk like that!"

"Don't mention that man to me Mary; you cannot know what he was like. You were so young. I sometimes wish we had never returned here, you would never have met that lad."

"Mam, I'm not listening to any more of this." Mary had heard these same words from her mother practically every day since she mentioned going to America with Martin. Her heart was breaking. She was so confused now and not sure what to do for the best.

The young couple walked up the narrow road towards the bog that misty day in late March of 1912. They were so excited about their big adventure. Going to America on some ship called 'Titanic'. Everyone was talking about this wonderful ship that had been built in Belfast. Martin was talking non-stop.

"Oh Mary, just think, my brothers said it's lovely over there; plenty of work and we can get married in a few years. I'm so excited."

Mary nodded but her mind was elsewhere. Should she ignore her mother and go, or stay and become a miserable 'auld maid' like her aunt.

"If you go Mary, you go without my blessing." These words seemed to be ringing in her ears for days. She was torn between leaving her mother but she loved Martin. All her young life she had loved this tall young boy, watching him grow into a fine intelligent, caring young man.

From their first stolen kisses and awkward fumblings behind the rocks on the shore at Milltown she had always known they would be together forever. Martin in turn had felt the same since the first day he set eyes on this golden haired angel with green eyes.

They had reached the stack of turf and Martin, looking around, realised how much he would miss this place, its solitude and the smell of turf which he loved. In summer when the bog cotton and heather blossomed it was a romantic, almost magical place. The methane gas at night twinkled like little stars on the surface of the bog.

Time was getting on, however, and he started to put some sods into the creel. Mary was about to tell him of her doubts when Brandy spotted a wounded bird and began to give chase. Martin was still filling the creel, not paying attention to what was happening.

"Brandy, come back," Mary was shouting, but the dog was not listening. She started running after the dog, not looking where she was stepping. This part of the bog had some treacherous patches, where many animals had been lost over the years. As she reached the bird she felt her feet sinking in the quagmire. Trying to free herself was making matters worse.

It was already much too late when Martin heard her cries for help.

"Martin help, I'm sinking. Help me, hurry."

"Hold on Mary, I'm coming."

Martin was running blind now, taking off his coat, he was desperately trying to reach the girl.

"Mary, catch the coat. Catch my hand. Oh God catch the

coat. Don't struggle, I've got your arm Mary."

Panic can so quickly replace common sense.

"Martin, please help me. I love you. Martiii..... Americaaaaa......."

Someone had brought a melodeon to Boyle's cottage and the 'American Wake' was in full swing. The house was full of people talking, laughing, telling tall tales and having a drink. There seemed to be a commotion on the road outside. It must be the young couple returning. Someone could be heard talking about Brandy acting strange and Mrs. Boyle went white as a ghost. The little dog never left Mary's side, where were they?

It would turn out to be a long, sleepless night. The old ones prayed unashamedly out loud around the turf fire. What did the morning hold? After all God was good. The dog had come and gone again towards eleven o'clock and the rain was now falling steadily. All anyone could do was wait for the morning.

The search party wound their way up the narrow road at first light. In the distance Brandy could be seen circling something on the ground. On closer inspection it was a half-full creel of turf, a pink ribbon tied to one handle. The whole area was deathly quiet and cruel, except for a pitiful, almost insane wailing towards the horizon, a cry which froze the blood of those standing there.

No one could be certain what had happened, but many months later the bog would give up one of its secrets. The body of a young woman was found by a farmer cutting turf. It was never known what became of Martin. However, on a certain March night each year neighbours would always swear they heard that terrible wailing sound coming from over the bog.

Were the young couple together forever, if not in America, perhaps on Irish soil?

Memories Runner-Up

Spring Chicken

By Nora Brennan
Castlecomer Road, Kilkenny

On a visit to Monaghan a particular smell brings back happy memories from childhood of little day-old chicks and producing food and eggs for the table

IT WAS THE smell that stopped me on the road. Something acrid and I didn't know what. A February morning, I had taken a walk along the narrow road towards Newbliss. Weeks of heavy rain had left the ground sodden and streams swollen. Frogs lay dead on the road.

Out past Annaghmakerrig Wood, sheep and long tailed lambs grazed on the brow of a dolmen, the field sprinkled with clumps of rushes. There wasn't a sound coming from the two long, low sheds by the side of the road, only the bark of a dog in a nearby farmyard.

Back at the house where I was staying, staff asked if I was referring to the chicken houses. "You're in Monaghan," they reminded me, and it was then the link was made. I was back in the late fifties, my father collecting day old chickens that arrived on the evening train from Monaghan to Thomastown railway station.

Monaghan was another planet to me then, the windows of my world going no further than the top of the haggard, the chapel by the stream and the two-teacher school at the Holy Stone. There was huge excitement in the house; the infra-red lamp was ready in the hay barn and I was eager to see the new chicks, to be the first to hold a pulsing bundle of yellow fluff in my hand.

My mother was at home rearing chickens. From shell to table she looked after them, and when there was money to be made from the weekly sale of eggs, she bought extra 'day-olds' from Monaghan. At Christmas she plucked and cleaned them for cooking, the rest of the family disappearing for fear of what they might see.

But I had seen her towards the end of the process once, the legs of a naked bird caught in one hand, the wing opened out in the other as she flashed it across the open fire, singeing off any remaining hairs or small feathers.

While the 'day-olds' were wonderful to see, it was the miracle of the shells cracking open with new life that captivated me most. I was in on the hatching from day one, eying the big brown hen as she squatted and laid her full body over the nest, making sure all eggs were tucked in beneath.

When the three weeks were up we inspected the eggs carefully for signs of chipping. Usually the chickens birthed themselves but now and then a weak one might not be able to penetrate the thick membrane inside the shell. In that case, my mother helped it along, picking away small pieces of shell, careful not to force.

'The important thing is to get the head out,' she'd say, catching the beak. With a slight manoeuvre of the head, she would ease it out, a damp, scrawny slip of a bird grappling with survival. 'The rest he has to do himself', she'd say, laying the egg down in the nest, safe in the warm overhang of the hen's bosom.

We went back to the nest several times the first day, discarding the empty shells of those that had hatched and helping others along. Soon the new-borns were on their feet, dry and fluffy, appearing and disappearing beneath the hen like ants beneath a stone.

Day after day I stayed close to the new arrivals, loosely cupping my hands to take one up, then placing it down gently, watching the chickens feed and drink from the lid of a sweet can or an enamel plate that had stones in the centre of the water to keep them from drowning.

Conscious of our three cats, chicken wire was secured around a cordoned off area and soon the chickens were scratching the ground, roaming around the haggard and finding their way to the hen house at dusk.

Hens' nests were clean, usually cosy corners in old banks of hay in the calf house, barn or hayshed that I think my father left especially for them. Once, a hen found her way to the lawn and laid eggs in a nest she created at the butt of the pampas grass. The house where the hens roosted at night was another matter. It had the same bitter, pungent smell that I got on the road to Newbliss.

Production of chickens has changed radically over the years and sheds are now commonly used to rear them. Yet, the desire to retain or return to the ways of the past is growing, a time when hens and chickens roamed freely around the farmyard and we didn't use words like 'free range', 'organic' or 'corn fed' about the food we ate.

But we knew the joy of producing our own meat for the table and having fresh eggs daily.

Short Story Runner-Up

OLD DOG, NEW TRICKS

BY RICHARD LYSAGHT
Walkinstown, Dublin

Vincent is getting a bit cranky in his old age and tends to live in the past with treasured memories of his late wife, and he doesn't have a very high opinion of modern young people ...

THE FIRST THING Vincent noticed when he entered the rest room was the glass bottle, complete with the model ship he had put into it, askew on the cabinet; the second thing he noticed was the young lad dozing in the armchair near the window.

"He would have to sit where the light is perfect for reading." Vincent made a clucking sound, as he shuffled into the room and sat in the armchair opposite the lad.

With a huffy sigh he opened the newspaper and tried to read, but no matter what way he twisted or angled the paper to catch more of the light, he still found himself guessing some of the words.

He glanced at the young lad. "Why did the powers that be have young lads coming here in the first place? Did they seriously think that these young lads would have anything in common, or even want to be round old fogeys like myself? Ridiculous carry-on."

He shook his head, feeling himself going down the fiery rant-path; a path that lately was becoming a slide. "But of course the powers that be know best. Doesn't matter what you think. No siree. When you're top-heavy with years, no one cares what you think."

He shook his head again, let out a wheezy breath of annoyance and thought about what had happened in the meditation class he had just come from. It was either meditation or bingo, and there was no way that he was spending time playing bingo. He shuddered, even in a meditation class he was being told what to do.

"I want you to sit still and follow the path of your breath as it flows in and out of your body. When thoughts from the past or the future come into your mind put them in bubbles, let them float away, and get back to following the path of your breath; this will bring you into the present, to what the present has to offer you."

The present; why in God's holy name would he want to be in the present? What had the present to offer him? Everything he valued, everything he treasured, everything he held sacred, lay buried in the past. So he ignored the advice, as he always did, and let thoughts of the past, of his life with his wife, Sarah, wash over him.

Unfortunately, wallowing in memories of Sarah brought aches of longing to his heart and tears of betrayal to his eyes, no matter what promises he made to himself beforehand that there would be no tears. And in today's session, as in previous sessions, he had once again evoked the disappointed gaze of Luke, the meditation instructor. This time, though, Luke's words of encouragement and understanding were seasoned with a thick coating of annoyance.

"Stay in the present, Vincent. I know it is not easy, but if you do, you won't find yourself getting so upset. The present has much to offer ..."

"That's absolute nonsense," Vincent said, stung into action by the tone of Luke's voice. "Present has nothing for the likes of me. What you're pedalling is nothing but regurgitated drivel." Vincent thundered out of the room.

"Luke will probably ban me from the class after my outburst;" Vincent didn't know whether to feel vexed or pleased, now that he was somewhat calm. He shook his head. He had been tempted to explain that his tears were the overflow of a deeply saddened heart that could only express such sadness because it had first experienced so many years of joy and happiness. But what was the point. He doubted that Luke would understand, never mind listen to him.

He sighed and looked down at the paper, but something flickering in the corner of his left eye made him look up. The television was on. "Don't get annoyed," he told himself and went back to the newspaper. This time he did better at deciphering the words until a screeching sound began grating in his ears.

"What the?" he glanced over at the young lad. The sound was coming from bud like things in the lad's ears. "Twelve- o-clock in the day and he's asleep in a chair with the television on, and cats howling in his ears. Mother of all that's holy, I give up, I really do."

Vincent was tempted to roll the newspaper into a ball and fling it at the young lad. The thought of doing so brought memories flooding into his brain. Memories of being roused from sleep by the yowling screams of amorous cats out on the roof of his back shed; memories of slippers being sent skittering along the roof and into neighbours' gardens, never to be retrieved because of embarrassment.

Of course, it was Sarah's fault that he had trouble with the cats in the first place. She was forever putting food out on the roof for them, as if having two cats of their own wasn't enough. But no matter how many times he told her not to be leaving food out for the stray cats, she always did.

"Sure, it's only bits of scraps that I'd be throwing into the bin anyway. And you know how I hate to waste food."

Strange how it was always sardines, that neither he nor Sarah liked, that managed to be put up on the roof of the shed. He was often tempted to quiz her about this anomaly but never could, not when she looked at him with those innocent grey-blue eyes of hers. What he wouldn't give to be looking into those eyes now.

He shook his head, which shifted the memory from his head but only as far as his heart. Again, he tried to read the paper, but the memory on its journey to his heart had left tears in his eyes. He dropped the paper to his lap, reached into his pocket for a handkerchief and dried his eyes, which only encouraged more tears to come.

"Get a grip on yourself," he admonished himself. He took a few deep breaths and stared at the young lad. "Still asleep are we? Of course we are." A sliver of annoyance cut through

Vincent. He took another deep breath. “And why should we expect anything different from you, when you, poor tired soul, have probably been up half the night playing one of those computery things.” Vincent nodded, the annoyance morphing into anger and driving some of the pain of longing from his heart.

Vincent eyed the lad, taking in the battered runners, the blue jeans with several diagonal cuts running up the legs of them, like as if they had been through a meat slicer; the yellow tee-shirt that looked like someone had splashed red paint on it, and finally the blond spikey hair, making Vincent think of a hedgehog that had strayed into a plug socket and gotten itself electrocuted.

But what made Vincent smile, with a malicious sense of satisfaction, was the gadget that looked like bat wings the young lad had resting on his knees. “Oh, I see you have one of those gadgety things with you, now, in case you get bored. In my day…”

He drew a deep breath, suddenly feeling tired. He thought about getting a cup of tea from the kitchen just to perk himself up, but chances were he would meet Luke, who liked to go into the kitchen for a chat after meditation was over, and Vincent was now feeling a niggling sense of embarrassment over his outburst stir within him. He decided to forgo the tea, at least for the time being.

He yawned, keeping his gaze on the young lad. “Imagine having that for a son?” He and Sarah had never had children. “Can’t be easy for the parents of sleeping beauty there, and that’s a fact.” Vincent yawned again. “I may as well join him for a few minutes.” Vincent closed his eyes and settled back into the chair.

A minute later he was sitting bolt upright, as what sounded like someone screaming after falling down a manhole, filled the room. Vincent opened his eyes glared across at sleeping beauty, who was stretching his arms towards the ceiling.

“Hope, I didn’t wake you,” Vincent said, in a gruff voice.

“What’ya say?” the young lad took the buds from his ears.

“Nothing, just wondering if you had a good sleep?”

"Yeah, I did, I'm knackered after training last night."

"Training for what" Vincent asked, raw disbelief in his voice.

"I play a bit of ball, soccer."

"Oh," Vincent nodded, reminiscing, "used to play once myself."

"Did ya? Were you any good?"

"I played for Bohemians once, but, unfortunately, I was prone to getting injured."

"Being good enough to play for them is really ace. I'd never be as good as that."

Vincent sighed. "You might be, if you really worked hard at it, put in the training, made big sacrifices," Vincent said, his voice rising. Maybe the lad would leave when he realized how much of a crusty old crab apple he was speaking to. "Same things you have to do if you want to achieve anything worthwhile in life," Vincent added.

"Yeah, that's what me ma and me da always says."

"Oh," Vincent said, taking a breath. "Well they're right. You're blessed to have such wise parents."

"They say that too."

"What?" Vincent said, a smile creeping onto his face despite himself, a smile that drew a wheezing laugh from his chest.

"What's your name?" the young lad said, when Vincent stopped laughing.

"Vincent."

The young lad sat up straight, a curious expression on his face. " Are you the ould, I mean the man, who puts ships into bottles?"

"I am," Vincent said. "Why do ask?"

"Coz, I think it's really cool."

"You do?" Vincent looked at the gleam of admiration on the young lad's face and felt a warm glow of satisfaction.

"Yeah, I always wanted to know how to do it. Could you show me?"

"Are you serious?"

"Dead serious."

Vincent sat back in the chair and shook his head. "Well, I

suppose I could, if you would like to learn."

"Yes, nice one." The young lad smiled and made a motion with his right hand, which reminded Vincent of someone pulling an old toilet chain.

Vincent smiled; he had never before seen anyone getting so excited about wanting to know how to put a ship in a bottle.

"What's your name?" Vincent said.

"Jordan."

"Like the river?" Vincent said, absently.

"Yeah. Ma says she's sorry now she didn't do a Moses number with me; shove me in a basket and let me float down the river Jordan."

Vincent roared with laughter and then held his side and shook his head. "You should tell your mother she has the wrong river; it was the Nile that Moses was put in."

"Was it?"

Vincent nodded, putting the handkerchief up to his eyes. "My God, haven't laughed so much in I don't know when." He gazed over at Jordan. 'Listen Jordan, if I'm going to show you how to put a ship in a bottle you are going to have to stop making me laugh, or I'll never be able to keep my hands steady."

"Right you be," Jordan laughed, getting up from the chair and almost letting the bat wings slip from his knees.

"What's that for?"

"It's a controller; use it for playing games: soccer and…I'll show you."

A few minutes later, much to his surprise, Vincent was manoeuvering a player around a football pitch and, a few minutes later still, he was whooping with laughter as his player scored a goal.

"Nice one, Vincent."

"Yes, it was, wasn't it?' Vincent nodded.

"Hey, Vincent, if you like I'll get another controller off one me mates, and we can play against each other."

"'Oh, I don't want to impose on you," Vincent said, his heart pounding with excitement.

"No sweat, I'll just leg it down the road to me mate's house;

you keep the hand in while I'm gone. Be back in ten."

Vincent laid the controller down on the chair, his mind pondering everything that had happened. A few minutes later he had decided what needed to be done. First he would go to Luke, apologise for the outburst, and admit to him that the present did have something to offer (though he would never stop day dreaming about his life with Sarah).

Then he would go to the powers that be and both thank and tell them that having young lads visiting the place was a really good idea. On his way back to the rest room, he would collect his ship-in-a-bottle kit from his room.

Beginners Short Story Runner-Up

THE MUSIC LOVERS

BY KEVIN LEWIS
Clonard, Wexford

Three friends enjoy a fortnightly ritual involving good music, a social drink and each others company, and lulled by the sounds and the open fire, they have a chance to indulge in some mellow reflections

THE CLOCK in Rowe Street church tower struck seven as Martin pulled his front door shut and shook the doorknob to ensure it was locked. Darkness had already fallen over the town and he turned his collar upwards as protection against the first drops of rain that were just beginning to fall as he set off up the street.

"Evening Martin," a neighbour called to him, as she arranged her empty milk bottles on the windowsill for collection in the morning, "...soft old night. Off to the MAG, are we?"

"Goodnight Mrs. Duggan," Martin replied. "Indeed it is, and yes, off to the Mag."

The MAG, Martin's thoughts centred on this word as he walked and he smiled contentedly to himself that Mrs. Duggan should be aware of its existence. The abbreviation MAG stood for Music Appreciation Group and he now recalled its origins and how he had become part of it.

A number of years previously two ex-seamen, Ned Carty and Tim Kelly, with a similar love of good music and a friendship spanning many years, began to meet on an odd Saturday night to relax with a glass of malt whisky, smoke their pipes and chat about past maritime experiences as they listened to the works of the great composers.

It was while presenting a programme of classical music on local radio that Martin – himself a veteran of many stage shows with several local music groups and an avid lover of opera and orchestral mediums - first made their acquaintances.

The rain was now falling with steady momentum, and Martin decided to shelter under the porch of the old disused cinema before attempting to tackle the hill up past the Military Barracks that offered little or no shelter.

As he stood motionless beneath the canopy, hands in pockets, his back to the now redundant billboards, he watched the rain beat against the Main Street in steady rhythm, the gutters by the pavement carrying the rushing stream of rainwater with its debris of cigarette ends and sweet wrappers towards the corner shore, like some great river racing to the sea.

Staring blankly ahead his thoughts wandered back to how he had first, at the invitation of both these men, attended these impromptu soirees on a very odd Saturday night before, eventually, entranced by the whole idea, he became a regular part of it himself.

The venue for these blissful hours of music and drink was the Carty household in The Faythe, a street steeped in maritime history. Here was the red glow from the fire, casting long dancing shadows on the walls and ceiling, as no artificial light was ever used during the playing of music.

There was the hissing of the ash logs, the aroma of pipe tobacco and the glass of Glenfiddich malt, which the two seadogs insisted was 'the best of Scotch!' Then, of course, on top of all this there was always the unfussy hospitality of Ned's wife Stella. It was all too good to resist.

The rain had now eased to a light drizzle and Martin set off again. He covered the last part of the journey in no time at all and arrived at the Carty house at seven-thirty. Ned answered the door and admitted him to the cosy front room.

Tim was already there puffing on his pipe. "Damp auld night Martin," he said. "Ye must be soaked are ye? Sit down and get a heat."

"No, not too bad Tim, I stood in under the Capitol for the worst of it, then made a burst for it." Martin answered.

Ned entered carrying the bottle of whisky and a six-pack of Smithwicks and placed them carefully on the glass-topped coffee table. "It's supposed to ease off altogether according to the forecast," he added as he left the room again to fetch some glasses. On his return he poured the three measures of malt and they each filled their tall glasses from the six-pack. They then settled down for the coming night's entertainment.

Tonight was Martin's choice and he produced the cassette from his pocket and inserted it into the stereo system.

"Well what have you got for us tonight, then?" Tim inquired.

"Oh a fair old mixed bag," replied Martin. "To begin I have Mendelssohn's *Hebrides Overture*, which we all love. Then I've a couple of pieces by Mozart, a song by Schubert, the *Wine, Women and Song* waltz by Johann Strauss and we'll close the first part with Cavaradossi's aria *E lucevan le Stelle* from Puccini's *Tosca*, sung by Mario Lanza."

"And for part two?" prompted Tim.

"Ah we'll leave that as a surprise for the moment" smiled Martin, a wistful enigmatic tone in his reply.

With the light extinguished the three men settled down in the firelight with ales and pipes as the opening bars of the *Hebrides* began to envelop the room. In the twilight Martin's thoughts centred on his two companions and as listened to the descriptive passages of the overture he imagined their days at sea.

Tim was the oldest of the three and was of a quiet genial nature. Small in stature, he was big in heart. His smooth ruddy complexion and wispy white hair somewhat belied his age and as he looked at him in the half-light, Martin wondered what tales he could relate of his days at sea.

Not many people knew that as a young man Tim had served as a crewman on a destroyer in Her Majesty's Royal Navy and seen active service in some far off war. He was not one to talk freely about his experiences in this conflict and Martin deduced they were perhaps too harrowing to recall. He now sat with eyes closed his pipe in his left hand and glass of ale in his right, lost no doubt in some far off cove, imagining the waves crashing on a rocky headland.

At the other end of the sofa Ned was also in a world of his own. He was of a completely different character to his life-long friend and, indeed, could best be described as stringent in the extreme. His years in the merchant navy had been hard and the discipline encountered had taken its toll, making him somewhat strait-laced in his outlook on life.

To while away his time off watch at sea he would lie in his bunk and listen to the classical music station on the ship's wireless. He sat now with his head tilted back and his lips pressed tightly together, savouring the moment while sipping his whisky and swilling it around his teeth and gums, like some dental mouthwash, before swallowing. Martin's mouth formed a closed contented smile, and he slowly sipped from his glass of ale before sinking back more comfortably in his armchair and stretching his legs out in front of the fire. The sense of quiet satisfaction between the three men was most apparent.

For his own part, Martin's musical interests had been kindled from an early age. He remembered how, as a boy, he and his late Uncle William would sit by the old Pye wireless in the parlour each Sunday afternoon and listen to such programmes as *Semprini's Serenade, Sing Something Simple* and Alan Freeman's *Top of the Pops*. Throughout the week it was *Friday Night is Music Night* and Alan Keith's *Your Hundred Best Tunes* and occasionally Tony Prince on Radio Luxembourg.

He loved all kinds of music if truth be told, and there were not many songs or tunes that didn't recall for him some kind of memory, be it a happy or sad one.

The voice of Mario Lanza, as the condemned painter Cavaradossi, singing the poignant *E lucevan le Stelle* from Puccini's *Tosca*, brought the first side of the tape to an end and the spool stopped with a loud click.

"Well that was very nice indeed, Martin," Tim said as Ned rose and turned on the light.

"Yes, very enjoyable," Ned concurred. "Throw a couple of those logs on the fire Martin," he ordered, "Stella will have our guts-for-garters if we let it go out." Martin obliged and prodding the red coals into a glowing flat bed with the poker, he placed two ash logs on top.

Tim poured himself another dram from the bottle of whisky and topped up the other two glasses of ale. "What's coming next?" he asked.

"Well I've chosen a few nice easy-listening pieces that should relax us totally," Martin answered. "Firstly we have a medley of Stephen Foster tunes played by a Brass Quintet that includes *Gentle Annie, Old Kentucky Home* and *Beautiful Dreamer*. After that we have the slow movement from Mozart's *Piano Concerto No.21*, followed by Thomas Moore's, *The Last Rose of Summer,* as used in Flotow's opera, *Martha,* and finally the time-honoured *The Lark Ascending* by Ralph Vaughan-Williams."

"Excellent choice," chorused Ned and Tim and all three continued chatting about general topics as they took the customary half-hour break.

The soft strains of Foster's *Gentle Annie* filled the room. The fire glowed warmly and the ash logs hissed their accompaniment. The shadows danced long on the walls and ceiling and the music lovers sat silently contented, lost in their thoughts and dreams.

Martin particularly recalled his memories of another Annie for whom he had had a fondness long years before but, sadly, his love of her was unrequited.

Before long the winding tape had made its way to the end of the reel and as the final high-pitched notes of the Vaughan-Williams piece saw his lark gracefully ascend, the evening's recital was at an end. A minute or two of silence then elapsed, as if allowing the listeners to recover reality from wherever their thoughts had taken them.

Just then the door opened and Stella entered carrying a tray containing three mugs and a plate of freshly made sandwiches. "Make some room on the table boys," she said, "I'll be back in a moment with the tea," and she exited back to the kitchen. She returned carrying the teapot and a cup and saucer for herself.

Small in stature, Stella was a lady of honest, easy-going demeanour. Her cheeks were flushed from the kitchen heat and her brown eyes were bright with a mischievous twinkle. "Well, did you all have an enjoyable evening?" she inquired, pouring herself a cuppa from the pot.

"Indeed we did...," answered Tim, "...most enjoyable. How are things with you Stella, were you out visiting?"

"No, I've been down in the kitchen all evening doing a few things."

The conversation continued between the four of them as they drank their tea and enjoyed the sandwiches. Casting a glance at his watch, Martin then rose from his armchair and stretching his arms outwards to the sides said, "That was lovely Stella, thanks very much. It's time to go now, I'm afraid though. Thanks for the company lads; are we on again for this night fortnight?"

"Yes," answered Ned, "I'm in the hot seat next as far as I know, so prepare yourself for some Handel."

"Fair enough," Martin responded. "Goodnight Tim, see you in a fortnight."

"Cheers Martin, take it easy."

"Thanks again Stella" Martin said giving her a gentle hug, "God bless you love."

"Don't mention it Martin, goodnight and safe home," she answered returning the hug. Ned handed Martin his coat and showed him to the front door. Both men shook hands and bade each other a goodnight. "This night two weeks then if I don't bump into you before that," Ned said.

"Fair enough," the younger man said as he turned to go.

The rain had long since abated as Martin made his way down The Faythe. He was warm and happy and refreshed from the evening's good company and admirable fare. The sound of a dog barking could be heard from somewhere up The Rocks and a wrought iron sign creaked in the very slight wind that blew almost apologetically. Otherwise the world was still.

A full moon had risen and was showing the spire of Bride Street church in silhouette behind the houses of Swan View. The distant clock of its twin sister, Rowe Street church, struck eleven and Martin quickened his pace. The earlier clouds had dispersed and the sky was now clear and full of thousands of shiny twinkling stars. It was a grand night.

Martin thought of the condemned Cavaradossi gazing skywards from his cell in the Castel Sant' Angelo and, glad that he did not have to face execution in the morning, pursed up his lips and began whistling the Puccini aria as he turned homewards down The Folly.

Memories Runner-Up

Annie the Shore

By Brian Donaghy

Derry City

Remembering the hard but happy life of much-loved 'Aunt Annie'

IF YOU WALK the little twisting road from Ballyliffin to where it disappears amongst the sand, you'll arrive at Pollan Bay in ten minutes. Ballyliffin is a typical Irish village - small and friendly, lying on the northwest coast of Inishowen in County Donegal. At Pollan you'll discover the pounding Atlantic, ceaselessly ebbing and flowing. A matter of yards away is a cluster of houses, nestling together for warmth and security.

Here at Pollan Bay is where we spent our childhood summers. Brigid McColgan, my grandmother, was born and lived here until she married and set up home in Derry. Her parents, Charles and Anne, and granny's three single sisters lived here, their days measured by the movement of the tides. I knew only Annie, the last survivor, for the others are dead and gone a lifetime now. But Annie will live forever in my memory.

I see her there, tying and untying her scarf under her chin - she always wore a scarf - as she chats and pushes her hair back from her strong, weatherbeaten face. Her hands are gnarled, her arms tanned and wrinkly from a lifetime's manual work. Since she seldom wore stockings, Annie's legs are browned too, from long exposure to the elements, and for footwear she has on a pair of men's heavy boots secured with coarse string.

She had a hard life of it. From childhood, she and her sisters herded cattle, sweated at the bog for turf and dug potatoes. Thanks to Derry's thriving shirt industry, many women made a few shillings sewing for the factories in their own homes and the McColgan girls took up this work too. 'Aunt' Annie, as we called her, spoke of nights spent hand sewing by candlelight and oil lamp.

The years passed and one by one the family died off, leaving Annie alone to see out each summer day and each long winter's night, her head filled with the sound of whining winds and of breakers booming against the rocks and shore below her old cottage.

But she came from a people tried and tested by hardship, sickness and death. For over twenty years she persevered stoically, in the face of good times and bad, with resilience, good humour and an unshakeable trust in God's providence. She prayed, constantly.

Aunt Annie had a deep knowledge and love of nature and many's the time she'd give us an accurate weather forecast based on cloud formations and by observing her companions, the birds and animals. She had an uncanny ability to read the water's changing moods and never underestimated the power of the elements.

Local boatmen consulted 'Annie the Shore' when they were anxious about currents in the Pollan area, for swimmers and fishermen had drowned hereabouts down the years. During storms of wind or thunder and lightning, she prayed aloud and gave everything in sight a good dousing with holy water. "Thanks and praises be to God," she'd declare with relief when all was over.

There were always a handful of hens around Annie's door and her "Chucky-chuck-chuck- chuck" to announce their meal times brought every bird, squawking excitedly, to the feeding dish.

And when the late August nights were closing in and Annie had taken her one cow to the ramshackle byre for the night, we watched, spellbound, as she squirted the hot, frothy milk into an enamel bucket with all the force of a power hose.

Once, the cow's swinging tail brushed across my face and I began to cry. Annie rose from her seat to comfort me, told me everything was all right and then allowed me to sit on her special stool. And there I remained, my child's senses absorbing all those timeless sights, sounds and smells, until the cow was empty and the bucket full.

Afterwards, we'd dive down the field to Annie's house for those stories! She'd give each of us weans a brandy ball from a wee jar on her dresser and then captivate us with tales of wee folk and hauntings, fairies and spells! Annie, the born seanachai (story teller), painted pictures of the most imaginative colours and designs as she enthralled her innocent audience with her tales.

How she loved us all. It didn't occur to any of us to doubt a word she said and all too soon we were called home for supper.

"God bless yez," she'd say, and sprinkle us with holy water from a big lemonade bottle as we departed, enriched by our night's ration of magic and mystery.

Annie McColgan, the last of her name, died in January 1968 and rests with her family in Clonmany churchyard not far from Ballyliffin. Their epitaph is inscribed at the foot of the simple plot: *McColgan Family Pollan Bay*.

Highly Commended

Short Story

TICKETS PLEASE

BY MARY CONLIFFE
Robertstown, Co. Kildare

Two young girls have an unexpected adventure when they take the donkey and trap to the local train station to collect some family visitors from England

MARY'S MOTHER often admonished her children with the words: "Now children, be sure to say your prayers every morning. You never know what surprises God has in store for you when you get out of bed in the morning." One incident in their young lives would attest to the veracity of her advice.

Twelve year old Mary lived in a railway cottage at the foot of the Slieve Bloom Mountains in the year 1962. Their family farm had a five-acre meadow lying on the far side of the Ballybrophy/ Limerick Railway line. Access to the field involved crossing the tracks and this, of course, brought Mary and her younger sister Teresa into a relationship with passing trains.

The sisters played the game of waving to the passengers as the morning and evening trains weaved their way through the green lush fields of Co. Laois, belching out smoke and sparks, causing the cattle in nearby fields to scurry for shelter. The children were chuffed and excited when their friendly greeting was returned by a smiling passenger.

Despite parental warnings, the sisters would say on occasions "Let's go for a railway walk, " and so the pair climbed over the stile, delighting in the game of 'Giant Steps' across the wooden sleepers. The picking of wild strawberries and raspberries on the high thorny banks was a favourite pastime during the long summer holidays.

The set times of the daily passenger trains presented no danger but goods and cattle trains could appear at unexpected intervals. Constant vigilance was required as bends on the track rendered the trains invisible with only their sound as a warning. The driver always blasted the horn and gave the young girls a genial wave.

The sisters often sighed "Oh, I'd love to be one of those passengers on the train." They made a mutual promise that one day they would make a train journey together. Little did they guess how that wish would be fulfilled!

The highlight of summer for the children was the annual visit from their Nottingham based Aunt Bridie and her daughter Angela, a girl of about four years older than Mary. Not only did the visitors bring a diversion to the humdrum country living, their suit cases were always filled with presents - whiskey, tins of biscuits, boxes of chocolate and always a beautiful new dress for each girl, chosen by Bridie from a leading Nottingham fashion store in consultation with Angela.

Anticipation of the annual visit involved washing of curtains, repairs to paintwork, scrubbing of floors and chairs, weeding of paths and flower beds; in short no effort was spared to have the house and garden in tip top shape. This year mother had a surprise for the girls: "Now, Mary, I am going to allow you collect Bridie and Angela from Ballybrophy station tomorrow; so go now with Teresa and prepare the trap." Meeting the morning train from Dublin was an adventure in itself and so Mary and Teresa ensured that the leather seats of the trap and its metal fittings shone with thickly applied polish. The reins and collar of Neddy, their pet donkey, received similar treatment.

On a bright sunny August morning the party set off on the four-mile jaunt to meet the eleven o'clock train from Dublin, following a hearty breakfast of porridge and home-made brown bread and jam. As usual, mother sprinkled holy water on the girls, Neddy and even the trap itself.

The sun was shining and the swallows were ducking and diving over their like streaks of lightning. Off they trotted delighted and proud to be in charge of such an undertaking. Managing the trap was no problem because Neddy was so familiar with the road he propelled them forward towards their destination.

"Be careful of the bends on the road," shouted Maurice Lamb, a local farmer bringing home his hay on a bogey with Molly, his horse. Jerry the postman on his large black bike shouted as they neared Ballybrophy "Where are you pair off to?" The two girls called out the purpose of their errand.

"I have a letter for your mother, so I will tell her I passed you almost at the station. That will stop her from worrying," said Jerry. Little did they know! The girls answered with their thanks. Excitement ensured that the expedition party reached the station well in advance of the train's arrival. Having tied Neddy to a lamp post and fed him a large fat carrot, the two girls began to explore the platform of the busy station.

Ballybrophy was a major hub on the southern route where steam engines received ample supplies of coal and water. It was a well-ordered, old fashioned station of muscular Gothic style built by Sancton Wood in 1850, with its tall water tower a major feature.

Beside the station was a little pub called the Signal Box owned by two sisters, Statia and Winnie Lamb. Passengers awaiting trains hopped in for a drink, exchanged local news and aired opinions on national and international affairs.

The busy men working at the station took no notice of the two children as they investigated the waiting rooms, ticket office and store houses. Then Mary said, "Look, there's a train sitting on that platform, lets look inside it." Teresa agreed and whispered "wait a minute until nobody is looking" and so for the first time in their lives the two girls, so familiar with the external appearance of a train, were now taking an opportunity to see at first hand what the train looked like inside.

Such pure joy and excitement! Having scrambled up the steps of the train they found themselves in a long corridor. The first compartment was empty and they rushed into it giggling and "shhssing" all the while. They tried out the long seats, inspected the overhead luggage rack and even opened the windows, all the while pretending to be passengers.

While admiring photographs depicting Irish scenery on the walls the girls heard a whistle, banging of doors and suddenly the train began to move. They screamed "Stop! Let us out" but the only reply was "Puff Puff" as the train gathered speed out of the station. It gave a short blast on its siren as it passed under the footbridge at the end of the platform and then emitted a long clear blare as it cut its way southwards into the long open country side.

Imagine the terror and fear felt by the young children as they set off on this inadvertent voyage into the unknown!

In a panic and in tears the girls dashed into the next compartment where a middle-aged lady was quietly reading Irelands Own. She looked up in alarm: "Children, what's up?" Through a mixture of sobbing and crying the girls explained that they had only wanted to see the inside of a train and the reason for being at the station in the first place.

"Oh dear! This is a non-stop train to Cork," sighed the lady. Mary was almost hysterical "Mammy will kill us!" Teresa kept repeating "Poor Neddy, Aunt Bridie and Angela!" The kind lady took control and assured the girls that all would be sorted out at the station in Cork.

"Sit back and enjoy the journey" consoled the lady as she gave the children some chocolate biscuits and a drink of lemonade which she magically produced. She said comfortingly: "Your mother will have been through such an anxious time, she will be so pleased and overjoyed when you both reappear safely this evening. Punishing you both will be the last thing on her mind."

Later in life Mary often reminisced on the kindness of the stranger who had come to their rescue. With the gift of hindsight as an adult, Mary shuddered as she remembered that the two girls at one stage might have tried to jump off the moving train such was their panic.

Eventually the train reached its destination. The loud demand "Tickets Please!" sent a shudder down the spine of the two girls. The lady noticed their increased anxiety and said "Come with me, I'll sort things out." The ticket checker laughed when he heard the story. Mary and Teresa were tremendously relieved as they had anticipated huge trouble for having boarded the train without a ticket.

The checker then spoke to a garda who was standing at the entrance to the platform. The mood of the girls immediately fell because, like all children, they had a fear of being in trouble with the police. As they were shaking and shivering from head to toe the big tall burly man approached and said "You are a right pair, sent to meet your aunt in Ballybrophy and you end up in Cork!"

He took their names and addresses and then invited them into a private room beside the luggage compartment. All the while the kind Samaritan was at their side and she now hugged them both to say goodbye with the final assurance: "The Garda is going to get word of your whereabouts to your mother back in Borris-in-Ossory. The ticket checker is arranging for you to have a nice dinner and then send you back on the next train. So, you will have nothing more to worry about, he will be on the train with you!"

Mary and Teresa were later to regret that they never had an opportunity to meet and speak with their saviour of that memorable day. A dinner of sausages and chips was eaten in the staff canteen. This was a great novelty for the girls as they rarely had the experience of dining-out.

Muted conversation reached the girls' ears making them aware that they were the subject of some conversation amongst the railway employees sitting at the trestle tables. They were bemused and amused by the Cork accents when greeted by the men as they walked past. In the following weeks the girls often tried to mimic the funny accent.

The return journey was slower because the train stopped at every station. Mary's glum mood continued, feeling responsible for the whole incident since she was the older sister. Teresa, on the other hand, continued to point out the mountain ranges, rivers and farms as the train trundled through north Munster.

Mary did remark: "Aren't we lucky to have met these kind people today, even the garda! Did you know that the police can be your best friend in time of trouble?" A quiet early evening train permitted the girls have a first class compartment all to themselves, supervised by the kind ticket collector who informed

Mary and Teresa that he had two lovely daughters of about their ages.

At Mallow station the man invited Teresa to wave the green flag as a signal to the driver that all was in order for departure. She carried out the duty with alacrity. Even down-in-boots Mary performed the operation at Thurles. The two girls felt a great sense of importance as the mighty engine responded to their flag-waving. The ticket man put his hat on their heads and demonstrated how to punch tickets. He even produced a bar of chocolate for each of them

At last they reached Ballybrophy. A welcoming party awaited on the platform. They began to shiver and shake once more, anticipating what was in store. Having alighted from the train they ran into the embrace of their family. "Now, never do such a thing again!" scolded their mother but Mary and Teresa sensed that the anger was only a pretence as relief all round was the primary emotion.

Later on their mother used the event to drive home a lesson, "Now you know why we should never miss our prayers every morning. God sent along that kind lady to your rescue. Oh yes, never ignore a mother's advice."

Their story became the talk of the parish. At mass on the following Sunday the parish priest made reference to the adventure of the two girls, citing the actions of their rescuers as examples of real Christian charity in action. He asked the congregation to pray for all who had come to the relief of two young people in distress. Initial embarrassment was followed by a sense of being almost heroes as neighbours and friends clustered around them in the church yard.

Mary and Teresa learned from the experience that when a person sets out with a fixed plan in mind, chance events may bring about unexpected outcomes. In truth, the incident probably reinforced the innate adventurous spirit of the two girls from Borris-in-Ossory.

Short Story

The Midnight Race

By Anthony Rooney

Kimmage, Dublin

Uncle Mick and others were involved in an incident with the British Army in Dublin during the War of Independence, but Mick was not prepared to take this lying down. Indeed, he went to the very top with his complaint ...!

SOMEONE (I think it was Henry Ford) once said that 'all history is bunk.' Frankly, I don't believe that statement would stand up to examination, but it does contain an element of truth. When historians relate the events of the past they concentrate on the actions of the major figures of the time, kings, generals, politicians, etc.

Where they fail is in not acknowledging the contributions of the common man, the little, ordinary man who, finding himself confronted by danger or adversity, faces the situation with courage and determination, and by doing so alters the course of events as surely as the great figures of history. Such a man was my Uncle Mick.

On a cold January night in 1921, when the War of Independence was at its height, Mick was spending the night in a lodging house in Great Ship Street in Dublin; at that time the term "guest house" was not in use. Great Ship Street is a quiet, cobbled street adjacent to Dublin Castle. At the lower end of the street is one of the three entrance gates into the Castle.

In the twenties the wall of the military barracks occupied the east side of the street; the west side was taken up by four-storey houses. Two of those houses, 9 and 10, were the property of Mary and Nellie Ward, who lived on the ground floor of No. 10 and utilised the rest of the property as a lodging house.

Dublin in 1921 was like a city under siege, a curfew was in operation and the streets were patrolled day and night by British soldiers. It was one of these patrols that entered Ship

Street on that cold January night, shortly before midnight. Why they should have selected the houses of the Ward sisters it's impossible to say, but select them they did and, as Shakespeare says, 'thereby hangs a tale.'

For Mick and his fellow lodgers, the first intimation of their coming ordeal came with a loud banging at the front door. When the Ward sisters opened the door they were brushed aside by a group of soldiers who rushed up the stairs, kicking the doors and shouting to the lodgers to get outside onto the street.

Frightened and confused, and in various stages of undress, indeed some without shoes, the lodgers (twenty-two in number) were hustled onto the cold street. My Uncle Mick managed to pull on a cardigan before a cursing soldier bundled him down the stairs.

The lodgers were forced to line up along the footpath while an officer, accompanied by a sergeant, interrogated them. The officer, a small man with a handlebar moustache, seemed to be in a permanent state of indignation. He asked questions in a snappy, high-pitched voice and, if dissatisfied with an answer, berated his captive for their stupidity.

As Mick stood waiting his turn for interrogation he felt the cold of the pavement creeping up his legs. It was part of Mick's philosophy of life that when presented with a problem one should always seek a solution. So, feeling the cold in his feet, he did what any ex-soldier would do, he began to mark time. To those of you who never served in the army, making time consists of marching while standing at the same spot.

Those around him were not impressed by his initiative; indeed one of the older lodgers warned him that if he didn't stop acting the 'eejit' he'd get them all shot. Mick, however, feeling that the improvement in his circulation was worth more than the approval of his colleagues, simply carried on.

In fact, he became so engrossed by his efforts he failed to see the officer until that gentleman stepped in front of him and demanded to know "what the hell are you at?" Mick snapped to attention and replied that as the weather was somewhat inclement he had decided to offset its effects with a little foot-drill. The officer looked him up and down.

"Old soldier, eh? Glad to see you're not all Shinners."

He fired a barrage of questions, which Mick answered clearly and calmly. As details of Mick's service emerged, it was obvious the officer was impressed. Indeed, he began to speak to Mick in a more friendly manner.

He didn't want to be in this "damned country," "this was not his idea of soldiering, running around the streets like a damned policed constable," "still orders were orders, eh? Job had to be done, eh? Law and order had to be maintained, eh?"

Now my uncle Mick was a man with many admirable qualities but, I'm sorry to say, knowing when to keep his mouth shut wasn't one of them. Sensing a softening in the officer's attitude, he decided to take the offensive. He expressed the opinion that the behaviour of the Crown Forces in this country left a lot to be desired. He would go further, in fact, it was an absolute disgrace.

He sympathised with the officer in finding himself where he had no wish to be, and he could well understand the necessity of maintaining law and order, but it was his considered view that the officer and his comrades would make a better contribution to the situation by returning to their own country.

It soon became obvious that the softening in the officer's attitude was but a transient phenomenon. When I say it was obvious I hasten to add that I'm speaking about everyone except Mick. Mick, alas, having explained the shortcomings of the British Army, had moved on to the defects in the policies of His Majesty's Government.

Meanwhile the officer's eyes had narrowed to mere slits, his breath was coming in short gasps, and, even in the poor light of a nearby gas lamp there was a clear reddening around his neck. Finally the dam burst, the officer grabbed Mick by the back of the neck, hauled him into the centre of the road, and shouted to the rest of the lodgers to join him.

In a high-pitched voice he told them that "if it is a bit of action you want I'll give it to you." Even in his discomfort Mick thought this was a strange remark since none of the lodgers had expressed the slightest interest in a 'bit of action.' Indeed, they desired nothing more than to return to the warmth and safety of their beds. But the officer was an angry man and angry men do not, as a rule, burden themselves with such tedious details as facts.

Having forced the lodgers to form a line across the street, the officer gave them his orders: they were to run to the far end of Ship Street, touch the castle wall, turn around and run back to the spot on which they were now standing. As an incentive to their efforts, he informed the horrified lodgers that the two men finishing last would be shot. He then took his position on the footpath, raised his arm in the air, dropped his arm and shouted "Go."

The reluctant athletes took off down Ship Street as if the devil himself were on their heels. To Mick, and three or four others who were in their early twenties, the bizarre race must have been frightening, but for the majority, who were middle-aged, it could only have been an ordeal.

Though they pushed their aching joints and labouring lungs to their limits, by the time they neared the end of the street it would be fair to say that the pace had slackened off. They reached the bottom of the street, jostling each other in their eagerness to start back to where the ominous figures of the soldiers awaited their return.

Mick jogged along comfortably at the rear of the group. He was surely the fittest man there and, had he chosen to, could easily have arrived back at the starting point ahead of his companions. But Mick was a proud, independent man, and he had no intention of dignifying the proceedings by seeming to make an effort.

However, he was prudent enough to see the merits in not finishing too far down the field. It was just as this thought occurred to him that he stubbed his big toe on the cobbled roadway. All thoughts of the race, soldiers and danger disappeared in a searing flash of pain. With his eyes closed, and his body bent double in agony, he hobbled along, oblivious to all but his pain.

When he managed to regain his composure and opened his watering eyes, he realised that he and a panting fifty-year old were vying for the unenviable distinction of last man home. If, as Doctor Johnson said, "the thought of hanging concentrates the mind wonderfully," the same could be said of shooting, for Mick, with a burst of speed which impressed the onlookers sprinted up Ship Street to the finishing line and, though not taking first place, managed to finish a respectable fourth.

Having established a distance between themselves and the danger zone, Mick and the lodgers who had covered the course, turned their attention to the fate of the stragglers. There were four of them, and it was obvious that they were beyond caring what happened. Three of them were reduced to a walking pace, while the last man staggered along in such a condition that it was plain that he had thought the matter over and now considered the prospect of being shot a preferable option.

It was at this point that Mary Ward showed herself to be a woman of great courage. Boldly she stepped up to the officer and warned him that if any harm befell these lodgers she would see to it that he was held responsible. The officer turned away from her and told the sergeant to "get this bunch off the street."

The sergeant shouted an order and the lodgers found themselves bundled back into their lodgings as unceremoniously as they had been bundled out of them. Once inside, the Ward sisters, to their credit, did all in their power to assist the more distressed lodgers, extra blankets were provided and cups of tea and cocoa were freely available. Finally, some semblance of order was restored and an uneasy calm fell on Nos. 9 and 10, but for most of the inmates it was a sleepless night.

The following morning Mick, and a group of lodgers met the Ward sisters in their front parlour to discuss the events of the previous night, and consider what course of action they should take. One speaker suggested they should approach the newspapers and have the whole shameful incident brought to the attention of the public.

This proposal met with considerable approval but Nellie Ward expressed some misgivings. They were living in dangerous times and it might not be wise to draw attention to themselves, indeed, her honest opinion was that they should "let sleeping dogs lie" and put the whole matter behind them.

At this point, Mick stood up and addressed the meeting. He agreed that bringing last night's outrage to the attention of the public would contain an element of risk, but, he said, "It would be a sad day when Irishmen and women were deterred from the pursuit of justice by the fear of danger."

"An injustice has been done," he said, "and we have a moral obligation to see that the perpetrators are brought to account." As Mick's oratory reached its heights, the listeners sat spellbound and by the time he'd finished they would cheerfully have taken on the British Army on the spot. The patriotic atmosphere was somewhat spoiled when Nellie Ward startled the gathering with an extremely loud burp.

With those assembled now ready for anything, all that remained was to agree on a course of action. Finally it was agreed that a letter be sent to the then British Prime Minister, Mr David Lloyd George. As expected, this task was delegated to Mick, who was left to himself in an adjoining room and provided with the necessary materials.

Mick's prowess with a pen was legendary among his acquaintances, and it would be no exaggeration to say that on that occasion he really excelled himself. He began with a graphic account of the previous night's events; he described in harrowing detail the physical and mental abuse to which the victims had been subjected. He described the terror induced by the death threat made by the British officer and the lasting and detrimental effects this would have on the mental health of the victims.

He then went on to describe the blameless character of his fellow lodgers, all of whom were law abiding citizens. Strictly speaking this was not true since two of the lodgers were barred in every pub in Dublin, and a third, Paddy Watts, had once served a three month sentence for assaulting a foreign seaman outside a pub on Burgh Quay.

Mick then went on by drawing Lloyd George's attention to Mary and Nellie Ward. Not only were these two ladies of flawless character and impeccable respectability, but over many generations many members of the Ward family had served with distinction in the armed forces.

He listed, for example, the Ward sister's grandfather, Andy Ward, late of Townsend Street who had served with Kitchener in the Sudan, Peter Ward, late of Benburb Street, who had taken part in the relief of Ladysmith, and last, but by no means least, John Joe Ward, happily still with us, who, while serving with the 11th Hussars, had his horse shot from under him at the Battle of Jutland.

To draw the letter to a close, Mick pointed out that as an ex-soldier himself he had every expectation that those responsible for last night's outrage would be brought to justice. However, should no action be taken he would have no alternative but take the matter further. With this veiled threat, Mick assured Lloyd George of his best wishes and brought his letter to a close.

After the letter had been read to, and approved by the Ward sisters and the lodgers, it was signed and despatched that very afternoon.

Now I should like to conclude this story by telling you that Mick's brave letter was promptly answered, but that would not be correct. In fact, I'm not sure if the letter was even acknowledged, but among Mick's family and friends it was accepted as a fact that Lloyd George not only received the letter but he was so badly shaken on reading it that he immediately initiated the proceedings which were to lead to the Truce in July 1921, and ultimately to the Anglo-Irish Treaty on December of the same year.

It is now more than eighty years since the historic events of the War of Independence. Over the years I have read many excellent accounts of the period; all of them cover in great detail the parts played by figures such as De Valera, Michael Collins and Arthur Griffith – and rightly so – but I'm sorry to say, not one of them acknowledges the part played by my Uncle Mick.

Memories

Our Faithful Friend

By Brendan Gallagher
Cloonacool, Co. Sligo

It was time to bid farewell to our quiet and gentle friend who had been a constant companion all through our childhood

IT WAS THE LAST Sunday of July 1954. The waiting started at 7pm. We four siblings peered out through the fogged kitchen window. No tears were shed but the skies poured down their moisture as mist fell thick and heavy that summer evening. Our hearts were heavy and a cloud of numbness came over us.

We had a view of the road from one angle. Another angle allowed us to see into Belle's bed in the hayshed, the shape of her body still in the hay. Belle would not sleep there again. Our eyes flitted from one scene to another sensing that both were connected.

We saw my father leave the house, cross the flagstones into the farmyard, close the gate and walk toward the road; a tall strong sheep farmer with a gun on his shoulder, head slightly bent, and a small dark red, aged collie dog trotting slowly by his side.

Belle was covered in mange and almost blind. She had been with us through all our childhood. Being a quiet gentle dog, with endless capacity for the rough and tumble of children, she allowed us to run our hands over her soft red coat of hair. She did not react when pushed, pinched or pulled.

A faithful, clever sheepdog was Belle and my father knew her value. She had helped him shift the sheep from the hill to fields near the house in lambing time. When dipping time came around Belle rounded up the sheep and kept them near the dipping troughs for long hours.

While the thieving sheep were attempting to break into the meadows to eat the sweet grass, she was off like lightning, chasing them up the hill.

She accompanied my father when bringing sheep to the railway station some twenty miles away. On one occasion during the return journey Belle had been left behind. There was weeping, wailing and blaming over the lost dog, fearing she would not come home. Two days later she arrived on the street, hungry, haggard and hassled but delighted to be back where she belonged.

However, time had slipped by and Belle was no longer young. Life and health were slowly ebbing out of her. To our utter dismay my father announced one morning: "Belle will have to be put down. It's dangerous for the children to be around her. That mange might be contagious".

My mother agreed that she needed to put her out of her misery.

That fateful July Sunday evening we were told to stay indoors. Only once did my older brother venture as far as the bend in the road. He returned with the news that man and dog were climbing the hillside.

Our hearts grew heavier with each passing minute. Sensing our distress my mother provided tea and chocolate Swiss Roll. Still we waited. It was not an impatient waiting, more an accompanying of my father and sadness for what he had to do. The two hours stretched out like catgut.

Finally at 9 pm. we saw my father come around the turn in the road, the gun still on his shoulder and no beautiful Belle by his side. There was more energy in his stride, relief showed on his face as he locked the gun in the brown cupboard in the hall, tied the key back on his belt and entered the kitchen. We were silent, not trusting ourselves to speak.

"Belle's suffering is over," he gently said.

We wondered how our father was able to steel himself for such a deed. Sensing how hard it must be, we were amazed at his courage and so did not ask about Belle's burial place. The secret died with him. On that last Sunday of July we children had come to know that life was not all sugar and spice.

The atmosphere in the kitchen lifted. I rubbed the mist from the window. The evening sun emerged casting shafts of yellow light on the damp flagstones, making them shine. For a long time we remembered Belle and often recalled the day my father walked across the street with the gun on his shoulder, Belle by his side and us four awaiting his return.

Short Story

ANGELA'S TEA LEAVES

BY JOE SPEARIN
Clonlara, Co. Clare

Jimmy always tried to avoid having his tea leaves 'read' by his grandmother, Angela, but on the night before his departure for America he was compelled to allow it, and there was a feeling of unease when she seemed reluctant to tell the full story ...

THE CENSUS of 1911 recorded the O'Leary household as comprising of four people, representing three generations. Jimmy O'Leary, 20 years old, lived with his parents and his widowed grandmother, Angela, who was 80 years old and was a cherished survivor of the Famine.

Their humble abode, a thatched cottage, stood deep in the wooded foothills of the Galtee Mountains. Travellers on the road between Clonmel and Tipperary often called to the homestead where there was always a welcome. Nomadic labourers, travelling from one place of work to another, rested and drank tea in the cottage.

Now and again a journeyman with a talent for music might be persuaded to stay for an evening, the fiddle being brought down from the top of the cupboard. Story telling and card playing were popular diversions at that time, and it was often later into the night before the fire was made safe and people retired.

Such happy occasions were never complete without the reading of the tea leaves, which was old Angela's speciality. Jimmy O'Leary was sceptical of the grandmother's fortune-telling. Content to just look on while she went through her readings, he always tried to avoid having his own cup analysed.

"What are you afraid of, Jimmy?" his father would say; "sure 'tis only a bit of fun."

Angela's patter was sometimes predictable: 'an encounter with a tall dark man' ... 'money on the way' ... 'water will be crossed'; these were frequent interpretations deduced from the soggy dregs at the bottom of his father's cup.

It was not surprising then when, some time later, the landlord's agent, who was 'tall and dark', called for his dues. Money was on the way alright, on the way out the door! And the dip at the end of the boreen was often flooded, so 'water had to be crossed' to make your way to the main road. Angela's foretelling had been deadly accurate, Jimmy thought.

"Come here to me and I'll read your cup, Jimmy," Angela would say, but he was always a step ahead of her; "Sorry Gran, I have it rinsed out."

It was in the month of November of that Census year that the letter from America arrived. Jimmy's uncle had emigrated years earlier and had done well for himself. He had his own construction company in Boston, where there was a building boom. "Send Jimmy over and I'll look after him," the letter said.

It was an offer that couldn't be turned down and Jimmy was excited at the prospect of making a career for himself with his uncle. He would travel to America in the New Year. Christmas passed quickly and by the end of March the one-way ticket had been bought, along with new clothes, footwear and a suitcase packed with shirts and vests.

A gathering of friends and neighbours on the eve of his departure saw the cottage full of joyful celebration of the young man's good fortune, but there was also sadness at the realisation that he might never return to his home.

There was no shortage of food or drink. Snuff, tobacco and porter were in abundance. People always found way of getting such luxuries when the occasion arose. Angela found herself in great demand for reading the tea leaves.

"Come on Jimmy," someone called out. "Let your grandmother see what's in store for you." The cup was scooped out of his hand before he could protest. A hush fell on the room as Angela examined the dregs. "There's water to be crossed," she began, "lots of water." This drew laughter from the crowd. How obvious, thought Jimmy.

"And there's romance," she continued, "two hearts close to each other."

"Good on you, Jimmy, first love," someone shouted. "Wedding bells, wedding bells," another voice piped up.

"Will you be quiet and let the woman do her work," someone else called out.

Angela rotated the cup, first clockwise, then anti-clockwise, angling her head to gain perspective on the random pattern of leaves. Normally fluent in her delivery of information, there was a certain hesitancy about her that was uncharacteristic. Feet shuffled and some people cleared their throats.

"Jimmy a chroi," she said at last, her eyes meeting his; "I see a warning in this cup, dark clouds around the letters T and L. You'll come across those letters someplace and when you do, you will understand what I am talking about."

She placed the cup upside down on the table, covering it with her hands. "I'll stop now," she said. "I'm a bit tired; I'll do no more readings tonight."

The uneasy silence in the room was broken when Jimmy went to the cupboard. "Anyone for more porter?" he asked. While he handed out the bottles he thought about Angela's strange caution. T and L, what was that all about? he wondered. Oh, why did she have to go and read that bloody cup!

In the rush and bustle of the following day the events of the night before were forgotten, and when Jimmy bade farewell to his parents at the quayside, his heart was light. On board the ship he joined with other passengers waving to their loved ones.

A young girl standing near him wept tearfully as the vessel's hooter blared out a long doleful blast. In a gesture or comfort, Jimmy placed a hand on the girl's shoulder. "It's not easy saying goodbye," he said. She turned to him and sobbed: "I'll never see them again, my mother and my father." He took a handkerchief from his pocket and gave it to her. While she dried her tears he wondered if she was, like him, travelling alone.

"Do you know anyone on board?" he asked.

"Nobody at all. I'm meeting my aunt when the ship gets to America. There's a housekeeping job waiting for me in New York."

"I'm going to Boston," he told her. "I'll be working in the building trade."

Her eyes were bright and dry now and with the sea breeze ruffling her dark shoulder-length hair, she exuded an air of sweetness and innocence, he thought. She was about his own age and he couldn't help thinking of how vulnerable she seemed here, in the midst of total strangers.

People were moving away from the deck rails as the ship left the harbour behind and headed for the open sea.

"Would you like some tea?" he asked.

"I'd love some," she smiled.

They found a dining place and he brought a tray with tea and biscuits to a table near a window, from which they had a view of the waves and the horizon. He poured the tea from a silver teapot and waited while she added milk and sugar. Then he extended his hand. "I'm James O'Leary from Tipperary, but everyone calls me Jimmy."

"And I'm Tina Lomasney from Cork," she said. In a split second a chill ran down Jimmy's spine and he thought of Angela and her warning from the tea leaves. Tina Lomasney, the letters T and L, the girl's initials. The biscuit he was holding fell back onto the plate and small beads of perspiration began to form on his brow.

The girl frowned. "What's wrong, Jimmy? You look like you've just seen a ghost."

"Tina ... Tina Lomasney, is that really your name?"

"It has been, all of my life. Why do you ask, is there something wrong with it?"

Now he was embarrassed; his complexion changed from ashen to scarlet. The last think he wanted to do was upset this lovely girl. He had to explain his reaction, so he told her about Angela and the tea leaves. As he spoke he saw here begin to smile. Then she giggled.

"You find all this funny?" he asked.

"Sorry for laughing Jimmy, but my name isn't really Tina. My proper name is Christine, Christine Lomasney, and I'm surprised at you believing in all that oul fortune-telling stuff."

Now he felt foolish for letting his grandmother's interpretation of the inanimate remains at the bottom of a cup influence him in such a manner.

"Can we go out on deck?" he asked; "I could do with a bit of fresh air."

They left the dining room and went walking around the ship. It took a while for them to get used to the rhythmic rise and fall of the vessel's movement. She caught hold of his arm once to steady herself. Her contact set his heart racing. They found an alcove on the starboard side where a framed map of America hung on the wall and they saw how close New York was to Boston.

"Can I come and visit you when you're in New York?" he asked.

"Yes," she smiled; "I'd like that."

They met again the following day and with each passing hour the bond between them flourished and grew. At night, if the sky was clear, they would stand on the deck and look at the stars. On the third night, with a chill in the air, he held her close to him and their togetherness gave him a feeling comfort and affection.

When a meteor streaked across the heavens, she cried out: "Oh look, Jimmy, a shooting star. Quick, make a wish." When he closed his eyes, she turned and kissed him on the cheek.

Surprised and thrilled, he returned the gesture. "Well, that's my wish after coming true," he said and they laughed.

On the fourth night of the voyage he was woken from his sleep by a commotion outside his cabin door. He dressed hurriedly and went out on deck where he saw people running around in a state of panic.

"The ship is sinking, she's going down," a man shouted.

"Jimmy, Jimmy!" he heard Tina's voice calling from where a lifeboat was being lowered. He went towards her, but his way was blocked by a member of the crew. "Sorry sir, you'll have to wait, it's women and children first."

With the front of the ship already under water, the stern was rising. Jimmy struggled up the incline. From the waters below he heard a man shouting. "Hey, you up there, we have room in this lifeboat for more." Jimmy climbed over the rails and jumped into the icy water. He grabbed hold of an extended oar and willing hands dragged him to safety.

As the ship began to slide beneath the waves, he looked up and saw it's name emblazoned on the stern, TITANIC, underneath which was inscribed its place of registration, Liverpool.

Shortly after the disaster a telegram arrived at the little thatched cottage in the foothills of the Galtee Mountains. The message was short: "Safe in Boston, will write later, Jimmy".

Angela was relieved at the news and she reached into the cupboard where she had hidden Jimmy's unwashed cup since the night of the gathering. It was time to rinse it out.

Short Story

The Miracle

By Elaine Cawley Weintraub
Ballina, Co. Mayo and West Tisdale, Massachussetts

The doctor was called to a second potential tragedy in the same house and was overwhelmed by a feeling of helplessness as he looked at the little boy in the bed. "It will take a miracle to save him," he thought with apprehension.

WHEN I was trained as a doctor I felt a great sense of importance and that my training would be of great benefit to the people of Ireland. I would be the one who would cure the sick and console the mourners. Indeed, I was going to be a great asset to the country.

That belief of mine was supported for a few years by the generosity of my patients, who brought me gifts that I did not need but had enough sense not to refuse. Many a bill was paid by a brace of pheasant or a couple of chickens and dozens of eggs. Then one day I was called to a house where there were a few children and the message was that one of them was very sick.

So, armed with my fancy education, off I went into the house where the sick child was and met the woman of the house, straight backed and severe as she was. I followed her into the room where the child was in the bed. He was so small that there was hardly a sign that anyone was in that bed.

He was barely visible, just a small figure in the middle of the big bed and the sound of breathing that was clearly a struggle. His little head was hot and I tried to look as if there was something I could do, by staring into his feverish eyes and looking into his closing throat.

The sense of dread that seized me as I tried to cool that forehead and pretend that I did not know that there was nothing I could do was profound. I looked at the woman of the house and felt the tears at the back of my throat but I spoke briskly:

"Mary you had better get the priest."

She made no sign of understanding the meaning of what I had said but I could see, looking into her eyes, that a light had gone out, but the back stayed straight. The child's father came in and took off his cap, looking at me with a silent plea as he knelt by the bed of his son.

"John, get up," she said; "we need the priest and tell the neighbours." Turning to me she said "you'll have a cup of tea doctor."

"I won't," I said but the tea came anyway and I sat uselessly drinking it. Before I left the house, the neighbours had gathered and the priest's sonorous voice led them in the rosary and I knew that the child would soon be carried on the shoulders of the men of the parish to the grave that they would dig, and that his mother's heart would be buried there with him.

It was a great lesson in humility to know that, despite being considered a man of great powers, I had no ability to cure bacterial infections and that little children whom I had often seen laughing and playing could be rapidly destroyed by diphtheria, or tonsillitis, or even a bad cut.

The years went by and I had almost forgotten the lesson I had learned when a message came from the same family. Another child was sick. I drove up to them as quickly as I could and again was taken into the same room where again the tiny body of a small child lay beneath the sheets, his breathing laboured, his face flushed and his throat closing in just the same way as his brother's had done.

"Will he be alright doctor?" asked the woman of the house and I could not look at her, nor could I answer her.

"Try to give him water and keep his temperature down by wiping his face with a cold cloth," I muttered as I made for the door as quickly as I could. Again, I passed the father at the door and turning to me he said quietly: "For God's sake doctor, don't let him die."

On my way back into Ballina, I raged against God and against fate. The feeling of helplessness that swept over me as I sat and stared at the fire in my house, embracing my own utter helplessness, was unbearable.

How would I go back and look at that woman in the face and tell her that there is nothing anyone can do, and that her children were born to die? "It would need a miracle," I murmured to myself and the word miracle triggered a memory.

When I was in the University learning the skills that now seemed so useless to me, there had been talk of a new miracle drug that would be able to save millions of lives by destroying bacteria.

I had not the first idea of where the drug would be or how I would get it, but even if there was the smallest chance that I could find the drug and give it to the child, I would be at peace with myself. That was the beginning of a long search. After many long conversations with my professors I learned that there was a new miracle drug being tested in a hospital in Dublin but it was not for use anywhere else.

I thought back to my training when the professors and the experts were followed by a group of us walking behind them like geese, not daring to speak or ask a question. Could I do it? Was I able to risk offending one of those Godlike figures and how would I make him understand the suffering of a poor family and my own desperation to help them, and to prove to myself that I was able to save a life?

It was the thought of Mary's face and her straight backed despair that gave me the courage to pick up that phone. I argued and I pleaded and tried to make the great man understand why this one little life mattered so much. He and I both knew that the child was one of many in the same situation. In the bigger scheme of things what did one matter, he asked, and all I could say was that I knew he was right, but that this one would break my heart and destroy his family.

Something about my pleading must have touched a chord. Perhaps he too had once stared helplessly at a small child and watched him die, but whatever part of my entreaties worked I will never know. I do know that in a softer voice he said; "I will send you the medicine in vials and then you must follow the instructions carefully."

Then, reverting to a brisker, more professorial tone, he added: "You will need to constantly watch the child day and night, with medical help, and keep accurate notes on the situation."

I would have agreed to anything he said, and I did, without knowing where I would get the medical help or how the medicine should be administered. The next day, I had the box and for the first time I held hope in my hand. The little glass vials were slipping out of my hands in my excitement and I had to put everything down and sit down to calm myself before driving off to the family with my box of what I hoped would be a miracle potion.

Going into the house, the sense of sadness was overwhelming and yet unspoken; the child was struggling to breathe and the dark circles around his eyes were hollow in his colourless face. "Is there anyone in the village," I asked "who has any medical knowledge?"

Confused faces looked at me, wondering why I was enquiring about something so unimportant in the middle of a tragedy, but a visiting woman said that she had done some nursing in England but she had not been able to stay to finish her training.

"Well, you have some training," I replied "and that's grand because you and me have to work day and night with this medicine to try to save this child's life."

Her eyes were like saucers as she backed away from me. "I don't know any new medicine," she said "but what the child has I know can't be cured and giving him injections might just make him worse. What if we kill him with this medicine that we don't understand?"

Standing there listening and pretending that I had no doubts or fears, I knew I felt the same way she did. The same thoughts were dancing in my head. More gently, I looked at her and said; "wouldn't you do anything to save this child?" and with the tears rolling down her face she agreed that she would.

Together we looked at the little vials containing the medicine and at each other. Our eyes locked and we nodded at each other and she held out her hand to me and that was the bond sealed. We were in this desperate game together.

The woman of the house set up two chairs for us with a blanket and then began the vigil, watching over the child whose breathing was ever more laboured and loud and then, frighteningly, silent. I prepared the needle using one hand to hold the other one steady and praying that if I did no good, I would do no harm.

He was a small child to be injecting with needles every four hours while my partner silently wiped his face with a cold cloth and turned him over in the bed. The hours rolled by so slowly; I was fitfully napping in the chair and jumping to my feet at every sound, and injecting the little boy every four hours.

"There was no sign of any improvement and the child's dark circled eyes remained closed and his breathing became even more shallow. "There is no miracle," I thought, as I dozed in the chair. "It's been two days now and he is sinking away from us."

And then suddenly, in my half awake state, I recognized the sound that I was hearing. It was the sound of a woman crying and I jumped to my feet confused to see my nurse bending over the child, laughing and crying at the same time.

"What is it?" I asked, hardly able to listen to the answer.

"He opened his eyes, doctor," she said "and his breathing is more normal. It is a miracle and whatever is in those little bottles has saved this child."

I was afraid to believe and I immediately became the official doctor. "We have to keep up this medicine for another two days, and then wait and see." But my heart was pounding and the feeling of lightness and happiness was flowing through me like warm honey.

For two more days we followed the rules of injecting and bathing and watching and the child continued to recover. On the fourth day, he was sitting in the bed drinking a glass of milk poured for him by a mother who shone with happiness. Myself and my partner shook hands solemnly and I realized that I had made no notes for the professor in Dublin, but I did resolve to telephone him and tell him that his miracle drug had worked when all else failed.

Now, and only now, could I call in the woman of the house and ask her: "Mary what is the name of this child?"

"Michael," she answered and then "and what is the name of that magic medicine you have?"

"It's called penicillin," I said "and it's made out of mould, the kind you would get growing in the plates and cups that you have not washed. It's lucky that scientists have nothing better to do than be looking at mould!"

"It is," she agreed briskly and so we parted, outwardly unchanged but inwardly each of us was changed forever.

Memories

The Food of Summer

By Nora Brennan
Castlecomer Road, Kilkenny

An annual gift from two decent neighbours of fresh salmon from the river Nore was a memorable treat for a Kilkenny family

IT WAS THE FOOD of summer, fresh salmon from the river Nore, no questions asked. One warm July evening recently while attending the sixtieth birthday party of a friend, I savoured the smooth texture of wild salmon straight from the river near her house. Mingled with its creamy delight were memories of Paddy and his brother Jack, our neighbours.

Jack had a shy reserve and didn't appear much by day but on summer nights nothing delighted him more than to head for the river, float out the cot on the black water and wait. With luck there would be a tug on the fishing rod and a surge of delight in him at the glory of his catch while the rest of the world slept. It was Paddy who bore the fruits of his brother's midnight labours.

I was in the kitchen one morning with my mother when Trampas, our sheepdog, created a rumpus in the shed. There was a rap on the door.

"Hello girl," Paddy said, as I approached. He handed me a plate with a large centre cut of salmon. Heavy as dead weight is, its scales were like newly polished silver and its flesh the colour of my mother's geraniums.

"'Twas caught last night".

"You're too good altogether Paddy," my mother said, as she came to the door. "You shouldn't have. Thanks very much."

He was already on his way, waving his hand and saying, "Good luck, good luck." The dog barked frantically.

Paddy seldom called to the kitchen door. Mostly I'd see him in the distance leaning on the handle of a shovel, talking to my father. They spoke a language known only to themselves and were always available to help one another when carrying out farm jobs like loading cattle or tailing lambs.

On rare occasions after his wife died, Paddy would be at the door with a bowl or plate, saying: "Would ya have a bit of sugar girl?" Sometimes it was butter. And always his parting words, "God blesh ya girl," before heading away, whistling a tune. I'd imagine him sitting at the table beneath the Sacred Heart lamp stirring a mug of tea and eating a slice of fresh pan loaf bought from Hennessey's grocery van.

My sisters and I had got to know Paddy's kitchen intimately during that time because his house was the first in our locality to get a television. Most evenings we hurried through our farm chores and then, much to the annoyance of my mother and with little regard for his family, brazenly appeared at his kitchen door.

Our only need was to see the latest escapade of Trampas in *The Virginian* or Admiral Nelson in *Voyage to the Bottom of the Sea*. Afterwards we scurried home, cossetted in the belief that there was always a hero and good won out in the end.

It was at Paddy's family home that many from the townland converged on All Ireland hurling final Sunday; the black and white television was placed in the window recess, the Sacred Heart picture was in a haze of cigarette smoke, the cheers were deafening when Kilkenny got a score.

Except for Paddy's annual gift of fresh salmon, I never saw or ate salmon any other time of the year. We had smoked haddock on Fridays and sometimes in late winter my father would buy fresh herrings on the quayside in New Ross. My mother, without hesitation, would clean them out, coat them in seasoned flour and fry them. The cats were already waiting for the remains at the door.

The day Paddy arrived with the centre cut of salmon all other food was abandoned. We removed scales and poached the fish in a small amount of boiling water, my mother all the time vigilant to see if the flesh had lost its watery appearance.

We dined like princes, each tasty mouthful a creamy blend of omega-3s and goodness we never knew existed then. What we did know was that we were blessed to have Paddy and Jack as our neighbours.

Short Story

Home From The Sea...

By Patricia Carr
Fanad, Co. Donegal

Two young men go against local advice and set out to sea to fish despite warnings of an impending storm. The catch is good but as they turn for home is their recklessness about to catch up on them?

THE SILENCE of the summer day was broken only by the lapping waves breaking against the sides of the fishing vessels twanging on their mooring ropes. Some of the more seasoned old hands scanned the sea and sky for tell-tale signs of the weather.

"I don't like it. It's too calm. There is a gathering darkness over Melmore and listen to the roar of the Limeburner!" said old Donnacha.

"We won't be pulling out, a bhucahailli! (my boys). Maybe I'm wrong, but I would rather be on the safe side!"

Donnacha was a sage as far as predicting storms was concerned and his word was law among his own crew. There was no argument, but differing views about Donnacha's judgement were freely expressed when he was out of earshot.

"It's not going to keep me back. With that ruffle on the water, we'll make a killing. Anton, will you come with me?"

Anton Dubh was brimming with confidence and Ned was up for the challenge. These two stalwart young men, their cheeks glowing and their voices blending in the chorus of a simple song, rowed cheerily out of the harbour. Their home made vessel bobbed gently as it breasted into and glided over the oncoming waves.

Soon they were heading towards the horizon. On reaching a selected spot, their small net was untangled and skilfully laid over the rippling waves. Land disappeared and a few squally but harmless showers swept over Murrin Hill. It was time to rest.

Ned and Anton leaned back at opposite ends of the craft.

They revelled in the ebb and flow of the early evening as they refreshed themselves with the contents of their two man-sized flasks. Between gulps and large bites from their baked bread, they kept up a commentary on the prospects of a good catch that night.

"Maybe it's that bit too calm," Ned voiced his concern.

"Aye but there is a brave curl on the water out here. We'll be going home with a net ragged from such a heavy haul- just wait till you see!" Anton replied.

"The daylight is on the wane, come on let us haul in and make for the pier." Ned said.

Together, hand over hand, they wrested the sagging net aboard. Its ample catch spilled into the well of the boat in a glistening, heaving slithery mass of confusion. As they turned towards land, Ned and Anton exchanged snaps of conversation, which were punctuated by hoarse cackles of laughter.

"It was well worth our while. Didn't I tell you there was no storm brewing!" Anton said.

He spat on his hands, rubbed them in sheer satisfaction and grasped a set of oars. Their good humoured banter, mostly to do with each other's romantic conquests, lightened the lonely feeling of the empty ocean.

The outline of the hills circled the narrow inlet like outstretched arms of welcome to seafarers. Now and then Ned broke into song and the melodious strains of his youthful voice drifted over the heaving waves.

An angry gust of wind, from everywhere and nowhere at once, doused the medley from his lips. In its wake the daylight fled, the travelling clouds were now laden with gloom and spits of rain splattered over the two hunched figures. The ocean heaved as if suffering from a violent attack of indigestion.

The small boat swayed heavily and helplessly in the swell. Holding on to each other and attempting to avoid capsizing, Anton assured Ned that this was merely a freak passing shower. Ned would not be assuaged and in time he was proved right.

After an hour or so the strong breeze whipped the spray against their ruddy faces and the cold air bit into their hands.

Their fatigue was replaced by a strange sense of energy and the will to hold on until the worst had passed. The storm seemed to have receded, only to come alive again with renewed velocity.

Pain and stiffness seeped into every joint in both men's bodies. Their limbs turned to a rubbery numbness. They lost their balance, both fell in such a way as to end up trapped under the upturned boat.

In his mind Ned was back home under the protective gaze of the Sacred Heart picture with its brown and cream contract of devotion, showing the family names in gold lettering. Anton was immersed in a halo of light and whispered what would most likely be a dying prayer.

A long thin dawn crept slowly into view. Word had spread fast and soon the undulating sand dunes were dotted with concerned neighbours. Big Mary led them in a quietly murmured Rosary for what, it could be assumed, was the repose of the souls of these two fine young men. The discovery of fragments of their wrecked boat confirmed this fear. For days anxious groups of locals scoured the coastline in a concentrated search for the two bodies. The ninth day had passed without a result and any remaining hopes were quickly fading.

Even the sea did not raise its voice to disrupt the quiet which descended on the villagers. Wake attendees made their way between one house and the other. Both families listened as the same words of comfort were offered, like the murmur of a slow flowing river. Ned's mother was in denial and felt as though she was just a spectator in this scene from the life of someone else. Anton's father, while trying to remain strong for his family's sake, was walking in a shadow that even the bright summer sunlight could not pierce.

These wakes were surreal. The light of the blessed candles on the small white-clothed table flickered sideways in the draught, almost dying out only to flare up again with renewed luminance. Anton's mother, Agnes, looking through glazed tears, fixed her gaze on the rise and fall of the light.

"Look at how the light is so flimsy at times that you would think that it's gone. At its lowest, it gradually comes back to life. That's a sign, I know it – there is still hope." Friends and neighbours pitied Agnes as she consoled herself with this soothing thought. When Big Mary gave out the Rosary that night she did not directly pray for the repose of the two missing young souls, though many felt that it was futile to continue to hope against hope.

The vacant days passed quietly, as the visits from neighbours gradually became less frequent. In a way, both mothers were thankful for a respite from the awkward condolences being offered in the same repetitive tone. On the other hand, their houses were enfolded in a shroud of emptiness, with too much unfilled space. There were no funerals to bring a sense of closure to the tragedy. Having no graves to visit meant there was no tangible link with the loved ones, even in death. There was a void that most likely would never be filled.

"Is fearr súil le cuan, na súil le h-uaigh!" Ned's mother, Kate, kept repeating this old Irish proverb, ("Better an eye to the quay, than an eye to the grave.")

Agnes and Kate made the daily pilgrimage. Together they could be seen walking the length of the shoreline, fingering well-worn Rosaries. On days when the wind tugged from every side, they leant against each other for support. There were times when Agnes was glad of the wind, which made conversation inaudible so that she could be alone with her thoughts.

On their homeward trek one glorious summer afternoon, Agnes and Kate dallied a while on the top of Currin. Through transparent tears, Agnes thought she saw a smidge of light on the far horizon. They whispered a joint prayer, begging the now tranquil sea to yield up its dead. As they descended from the vantage point, they little thought that the answer to their entreaty could not and would not come from the sea!

As they skirted the arc of the bay, a medley of cheers and triumphant whoops wafted over the calm water from the direction of the pier. Coming nearer, Agnes and Kate noticed half built hay cocks left in tumbledown straggly heaps in the fields. The cluster of houses that formed the heart of the village came in sight. The neighbourhood had put life on hold to converge either side of the burn from which the townland took its name.

Old Johnny Brieny's accordion belted out a wheezing version of "The Bluebell Polka", to which six couples battered a set dance on the cobbles. The reality of the situation was put beyond doubt. Agnes and Kate watched as the eager crowd parted, cutting a swathe for two young men being carried shoulder high. Agnes felt a lightness in her head, her legs wobbled underneath her- and the sun's light was quenched.

She came to in the comfort of her own fireside chair. She rose eagerly to embrace Anton and showered him with a wave of tears that had been welling up since his disappearance.

"Hold on, Mammy," he joked "I was nearly drowned once, that was enough!"

"Now, Anton," Ned rebuked, "you should not make light of it - but for the grace of God and the quick action of that Downings boat- we were gonners."

Even though both men had already narrated the account of their rescue many times, they seemed to revel in repeating it over again. Ned's memory of it came and went in snatches. He remembers both of them drifting with the wayward vessel until it crashed against something solid.

That object was no more than a rock, the tip of which was protruding above the water line. Ned managed to balance himself on a large plank of wood from the stricken boat while he hauled Anton behind and both of them fell exhausted onto the frail solidity of the outcrop.

They heard voices, distant and yet close at hand. Were these more wild imaginings of two desperate men?

Ned and Anton were now so traumatised by their experience that the balance between reality and fantasy had become indistinct. From within the mist, the skipper of the "Máthair Dé" trained a beacon onto the two hunched figures. Threshing its way towards them in defiance of the angry swell, the "Máthair Dé" was now within hailing distance.

To Ned and Anton hands appeared out of the froth of the sea. It was almost like the hand of God reaching from the lining of a cloud. They felt themselves being dragged and dunked amid a torrent of curses. After they regained consciousness, the serene calm of their surroundings was hard to fathom.

Back on dry land once more Anton and Ned were taken to Mickie Báns in Downings. They were treated like Mickie's own family and given the run of the house. This time Anton and Ned heeded the advice they were given and stayed with Mickie for a week until the shock of their narrow escape had begun to fade. Word of their dramatic rescue was a topic of discussion within this close-knit fishing community. Communications of the time were limited and getting word to their families was another challenge. Ned and Anton met this head on and set out on foot for the arduous trek home.

Here they were now – mentioned men in the parish! Their encounters with the sea did not end there as Anton and Ned embarked on a voyage to a new life in America. On his first visit home, forty years later, Ned took a stroll down by the newly refurbished harbour. He marvelled at the number of the boats there, and the array of modern technological navigation aids on board. As he watched them launch out on the waters under a leaden sky, he turned to Anton and said:

"There's every sign of a storm – when will the young ones learn a lock of sense!" And they both laughed!

Memories

A Click From The Hall

By Linda Guerin
St. Patrick's Road, Limerick

Remembering a time when the electricity was kept going by inserting two-shilling pieces into the meter in the hall whenever there was a black-out, and these could often occur at the most inopportune times

ALL THE TALK of austerity in the last few years put me in mind of the way my family settled electricity bills in the 1960s. We lived in Limerick city and my parents availed of the 'pay-as-you-go' system that was available at the time.

It was all done manually. If memory serves me correctly there was a slot on the face of the meter for florins. A black, metal box hung below the meter like a savings box to collect the coins.

Whenever we ran out of credit, a loud click could be heard from the meter in the hall. Then a power cut struck the house. The lights went out. Electrical appliances stopped working until my father or mother pushed a florin through the slot in the meter.

The task of feeding the meter usually fell to my parents. However, if they were not available I would carry a kitchen chair out to the hall, climb up on it and have the pleasure of pushing a florin through the slot.

Of course, when the bill arrived the black box was choc-a-block with coins. Then my father would carefully remove the heavy box from below the meter and leave it on the kitchen table for my mother. She would put it in her shopping bag and carry it down to the showrooms on O'Connell Street to pay the electricity bill.

Sometimes my mother waited until Saturday to pay the bill. She often asked me to carry the box of coins for her. It felt like a ton weight. On entering the showrooms I would quickly push the black box on to the counter. Then, I took the opportunity to wander around the brightly-lit premises. The gleaming, new electric cookers always caught my eye and the coal-effect fires seemed very cosy.

I seem to remember that the counter assistant had to unlock the black box before she could count the coins. The total was subtracted from our electricity bill. My mother would pay the balance.

As the years passed, the black box showed itself to be a ruthless tyrant. It seemed to gobble coins faster than a slot machine in an amusement arcade. I remember one night I was sitting in a bathtub of soapy water listening to voices and music from the television downstairs. Suddenly a loud click came from the electricity meter in the hall. A heartbeat later the bathroom was plunged into darkness and the television fell silent.

Then pandemonium broke out. The kitchen door opened and my father called out, "Where are the matches?"

I heard my mother rummaging in the press in the kitchen. "Try your pockets," she said.

Sitting in the bathtub I pictured the frantic search of drawers, pockets and purse for the much needed florin that would light up the house. I waited and waited. Then, another click came from the meter in the hall as my father pushed the coin through the slot. A few seconds later the light came on in the bathroom and the television resumed its broadcast. We were not a well-organised family. No one ever thought to have a torch standing by.

Coming up to the Christmas holidays my parents used to hoard coins for the black box. With the shops closed on Christmas Day and St. Stephen's Day it would have been difficult to get change if we ran out of credit.

I recall one Christmas morning my father was making last minute adjustments to the fairy lights on the Christmas tree. He had bought a magnificent set of lights in a shop in William Street. They had been designed in the shape of cinderella-pumpkin carriages. Everyone admired them. They had been twinkling and casting colourful reflections on the tinsel and the baubles during the whole of Christmas week. However, for some reason, they had stopped working on Christmas Day.

Undaunted, my father tightened the bulb in each carriage. Half-way along the set of lights he found a loose bulb. I waited with bated breath to see if the cinderella-pumpkin carriages would once more cast their magical spell over the living room.

My father pushed the plug into the socket. A flash of glowing light enveloped the Christmas tree. With a smile on his face he picked up a box of matches from the mantelpiece to light the white, cube-shaped candle at the centre of the dining table. Then he set off for the kitchen to light a fire for my mother.

What with relatives visiting the house, movies to watch on television and comic annuals to read beside the warmth of the coal-effect electric fire, the morning seemed to pass quickly. Then the moment arrived when my mother placed the hot, golden-brown turkey on the dining table which was decorated with festive crackers.

Everyone sat down and made toasts with glasses of lemonade. Just as I was about to sample some of the steaming hot, roast potatoes I heard a familiar click from the meter in the hall. We had run out of credit on Christmas Day.

The television screen went dark, the cinderella-pumpkin lights winked out on the tree, the warm glow of the coal-effect fire dimmed and the overhead light went out. But this time we were not plunged into darkness. The flickering flame of the white candle at the centre of the table lit up our faces and picked out the location of my parents' hoard of coins on the mantelpiece. Christmas Day was saved.

The oil crisis of the early 1970s sounded the death knell for the black box. At first the box had been a useful way to save for the two-monthly electricity bill. But, as time wore on the black box could not keep up with inflation. My mother found that she had to carry it down to the showrooms every month instead of every two months.

The end came when the black box filled up with coins after only two weeks. My parents made the decision to have it taken out. From then on there were no more clicks from the meter in the hall.

It is interesting, though, that some companies have re-introduced a 'pay-as-you-go' kind of system once again as we come out of our latest financial crisis and the cost of electricity is once again proving a heavy burden for some families.

Short Story

A Mother's Tenacity

By Kenneth Knight
Artane, Dublin

The mother of a Down's syndrome man worries about government cutbacks impacting on his job and tries to do something about it

AS BREDA turned into the car-park that fronted Furlong's furniture store, Des, as usual, was waiting outside the shop. With his satchel slung over his shoulder, he watched as his mother steered the car to the store's entrance. Just as she stopped a young woman left the store. She said a cheery goodbye to Des and got a shy smile in return. Des placed his satchel carefully on the car's back seat and climbed into the front. He nodded a greeting to his mother as he put on his seatbelt.

"Hi love," said Breda. "How was your day?"

"Ok. That was Linda." Des nodded in the direction of a small red car that the woman who had left the store was just getting into.

Breda smiled. "I know. How about pizza for tea?"

"Double cheese?"

"Of course."

Des nodded with satisfaction. Double cheese was his favourite.

Breda pulled away from the kerb, heading for the car-park's exit.

Finishing their pizza, Breda carried the two plates over to the sink. "Get the computer Des, we'll Skype Gary."

Apart from Des, Breda had two other children, Gary who was nearly fifty and lived in Toronto and Catherine, five years younger and living in Bahrain. Des came a distant third, twelve years younger than Catherine. Skype was a godsend for Breda, allowing both herself and Des to keep in contact with the others, although she sometimes felt out of her depth dealing with broadband connections, IP addresses and the myriad other things involved in the computer world.

However, as long as all she had to do was click on the little icon that was on the screen and she was magically connected to the other side of the world, then for Des's sake she would stick with it.

Des looked at his watch, knowing but not really understanding, that Gary was on a different time than he was. "It's lunchtime in Canada, Des. Gary will be at home."

Gary's face appeared on the screen.

"Hi Des, how are you? Hi mum."

"Hi Gary" they both echoed.

"How's work going Des; still on a three day week?"

Des's work placement in Furlong's was a three day a week affair. The other days were spent in the St. Michael's House facility near home. The St. Michael's House staff were all excellent in trying to offer their pupils some real life experience, seeing it as essential to their development. They had developed good contacts in the community over the years and local businesses were always willing to provide some part-time job opportunities for St. Michael's House members.

It didn't always work out and Des had been placed in some jobs he just hadn't liked. "Getting the right fit" was how Derek Brady, the St. Michael's House administrator, had put it to Breda at a discussion concerning Des.

Well, Furlong's was the right fit for Des. From the day he'd started there he'd taken to it like a duck to water. He loved all the staff, hero-worshipped the manager, Mr. Harrington, whom he only ever referred to as Mr. Harrington and never as Liam, and adored Linda, the accounts clerk. If the point of such work placements was to help those like Des gain independence, develop socially and enjoy life more, then Furlong's gave it to him in spades.

"Any promotions yet, Des?" asked Gary. "You should be moving up the ranks in Furlongs now."

"Gary, Mr. Harrington told me he couldn't do without me," said Des.

"That's what to do Des, make yourself indispensable." Gary smiled across thousands of miles at his younger brother.

"How are you mum?" he asked Breda.

"Ok son. How are you?"

"Grand. What's the situation with Des's work placement?"

"I'm going to see Derek Brady on Monday and after that I'm going to go to our TD. He has a clinic outside the shopping centre."

"Good."

Des's job in Furlongs involved cleaning the furniture, hoovering the store and helping move the stock around. Fairly simple to be honest, but from his first day there he had absolutely loved it. From the beginning of the week he looked forward to Wednesday, Thursday and Friday, his three days in Furlong's and he spent hours on Tuesday evening preparing for his 'week's' work.

Now, due to government cutbacks, Breda had heard there was a possibility that Des could lose this little job and it was breaking her heart to think what this would do to him. She'd barely slept since she had heard this news and was worried sick.

She'd told both Gary and Catherine about her fears, but living halfway around the world, there was nothing they could do to help. Breda felt a little guilty about burdening them with something they could do nothing about, but she had needed to tell someone.

After a bit more chat with Gary, she and Des said their goodbyes and logged off. "We'll talk to Catherine tomorrow Des," said Breda, as she went to make a cup of tea.

"Thanks for coming in to see me, Mrs. Keegan."

Breda was sitting in Derek Brady's office in St. Michael's House on the following Monday morning. "Is there any truth, Mr. Brady, in the rumours I've heard about Des's work placement?"

Derek Brady produced a wry smile. He had to admit, dealing with people like Breda Keegan, or indeed any of the parents of his Down's Syndrome 'pupils' at St. Michael's House, was like a breath of fresh air. No time for beating about the bush, just straight to the point. He found it terrifically refreshing. As a result, he always dealt with them the same way.

"I have to admit, Mrs. Keegan, there is a threat to his job with Furlong's."

Breda felt her hands clench each other. Helping Des through his daily life was her one and only concern and anything that threatened that produced a fear and fury combination in her.

"How so?"

Derek Brady leaned forward. "Part of the payment Des receives for his work in Furlong's comes from a government subsidy. There is the possibility that this subsidy may be withdrawn."

"That would mean him losing his job?"

"Possibly, but this is not cut and dried yet. It's still just a possibility."

"How are you, Mrs. Keegan? How can I help you?"

Breda shook the proffered hand. Dry and surprisingly warm, it belonged to her local TD, David Wilkes. They were in his 'clinic', a tiny caravan that was parked opposite Dunne's Stores every Saturday morning.

"I hope you *can* help me, Mr. Wilkes. My son Des is 32 and he's a Down's syndrome man."

Wilkes was taking notes.

"Three days a week he works in Furlong's Furniture, beside the big Dulux store."

"Yes, I know it. Nice shop."

"It's part of a work placement scheme that was organised for him by St. Michael's House."

"Mm hm." The TD was still taking notes.

"Well, I've been told that with government cutbacks Des may lose this job."

Wilkes stopped writing and gave Breda his full attention.

"To Des a job like this is a godsend. What he earns is unimportant, but just being out there in the world is brilliant for him. It gives him independence, confidence, a feeling of worth."

"I'm sure it does, Mrs. Keegan. Like us all, we just want to be valued." The TD smiled at his own irony. He took up his pen again. "What exactly have you been told?"

"Derek Brady, the St. Michael's House administrator, told me that there is a possibility, that due to government cutbacks, the subsidy that is paid to Furlong's to employ Des may be withdrawn. If that happens he could end up losing his little job."

"Mmm." The only sound was the TD's pen scraping along his notebook.

"You see, Mr. Wilkes, Des can't express exactly what this job means to him. He doesn't have the words. But I know, because I can see it in him. He loves working there. He takes what he does very seriously, even if it's only helping with stock deliveries, cleaning the furniture, or hoovering the showroom. It's really good for him."

"I agree with you, Mrs. Keegan. Schemes like this are worth their weight in gold for special needs people like Des. Unfortunately, they're often the first to be hit when things are tight." He stapled all his notes together. "I'll get on to the Minister and find out what I can about any cutbacks in this area. I'll also let him know your own concerns and the impact it would have on Des for these subsidies to be withdrawn."

Later that day, as Breda sat in her favourite chair with a cup of tea, she looked at a photograph of her husband, John, Des's dad. Dead nearly twenty years, Breda still ached for his presence. She had always felt that they would share the worries and concerns of Des's life together, but a pulmonary embolism on a summer evening had put paid to that. Now it was up to Breda – bureaucracy, administrators, TD's, even computers. At 72 she often felt worn out with it all, but then a smile from Des acted like an adrenaline rush to her spirits. "You took the easy way out," she gently admonished John's photograph.

Standing up stiffly she brought her cup to the sink. The she opened up her laptop. Her daughter Catherine had suggested that she write a letter to all her local representatives, explaining to them the huge impact such niggardly cutbacks would have on the lives of Des and others like him. "Start a campaign mum", Catherine had suggested. Well, Breda didn't know about a campaign, but she could certainly write a few letters.

Forty five minutes later Breda sighed and sat back in her chair. She'd composed a letter and e-mailed it to all of her local representatives. In addition, she'd also e-mailed it to one local and two national newspapers. As she closed the laptop she had no idea of the storm she'd unleashed.

By midday the following day she'd had at least ten telephone calls. Several were from people who knew her and Des and had read her letter, which had already been published in both national newspapers. Other calls came from parents who also had special needs loved ones, all of them offering their support.

One call was from a radio station who wanted to interview her – Breda nearly passed out at this. On checking her e-mails and she found about a dozen messages there. One was from a newspaper where her letter had been published and they also wanted to interview her. Whether Breda liked it or not, her 'campaign' had begun.

Suddenly everyone was talking about cutbacks to the 'special needs subsidy', as it became known. Politicians were debating it and it was discussed on current affairs programmes on radio and television. A journalist for a Sunday newspaper wrote a long article in which he praised Breda for taking on the might of the State and called her an unlikely hero. She almost died when she read it.

Both Gary and Catherine picked up the story and Catherine called her an ambassador for the downtrodden. Every time Breda went outside people were shaking her hand and congratulating her. Embarrassed though she was, Breda put up with it all, since she knew that this could only be good for Des's situation.

Des, meanwhile, just went about his business, oblivious to the debate about his job. For Breda this was the thing to hold on to, Des was just Des. He was her main source of worry and her main font of happiness, just as he always had been. Whatever he needed her to do she would do, just ask the government! She smiled at John's photograph, hoping he'd be proud of her

Memories

'Is That You Eily?'

By Eileen Caplice
Mallow, Co. Cork

The little girl had the habit of calling to see an 'old' lady on her way home from school and she always got a warm welcome and memories that would last forever

THE TURF SMOKE rising high above the thatch told me that Mrs. Hennessy was home. I stopped and parked close to the ditch, the road being narrow. I walked to her front door inhaling the smell of burning turf. It transported me back nearly fifty years. Where have fifty summers gone, I wondered!

I knocked gently as I had so many times all those years ago. Momentarily, I heard the familiar creaking of the sougan chair and then the unfamiliar sound of shuffling on the stone floor inside. (I berated myself silently for postponing this visit). Then, a jangling of keys and I watched the latch lifting. The sound was music to my ears and flung me back through a time-tunnel of nostalgia.

The door opened slowly. I remembered Mrs. Hennessy peering down on me as a child but where was she now? Suddenly, I was looking down on her. We had traded places and I was shocked. She put her old white hands with blackened nails on top of the half-door and pulled herself forward to see who was on the other side.

"Who have I at all?" I heard her mumble into her chest. "It's me Mrs. Hennessy" I said. There was a pause. I knew she was thinking, so I gave her time. Then, with great effort she lifted her head slowly and asked in the same voice that I recalled immediately "is that you Eily?"

Time had taken its toll on this once tall, elegant woman who was now hunched, shrunken and riven with arthritic pain. Her sharpness was still there, though she had surrendered now to old age. I passed her cottage every day on my way home from school. At that time, in the 1950s, when infant classes finished at 2 o'clock, there were no cars waiting to collect us so we wandered home alone.

While I waited for my older siblings to catch up, I visited Mrs. Hennessy. I would knock on the half-door and she would call out "is that you Eily?" I would call back "it is". She would lift the latch of the full door and pull back the timber sliding catch of the half-door.

"Could I have a drink of water please," I would ask. "Of course you can Eily, come in" was always the reply. When I grew tall enough to see over that half-door, it gave me great confidence. When I could reach over and unlatch it from the inside, I thought I had 'arrived'.

Once inside, it was sweetened tea and two Marietta biscuits, so delicious after a long day at school. She allowed me to lift the wire mesh cover and help myself to an apple or a pear from her own garden. I sat on her sougan chair and turned the wheel that blew the bellows and reddened the sods.

This delighted her as she needed a good fire for boiling water, cooking and baking in the bastible. I helped her to lift the heavy iron black skillets onto the crane that swung over the flame. Of course, she always took the brunt of the load. From her sougan chair, I looked up the chimney to see the blue sky. When it rained, blackened drops landed in my tea. Sometimes hailstones shot down the chimney and made hissing noises around the hearth.

At autumn time she took me to her orchard to collect apples. She held out her apron while I filled it with windfalls. I picked her black and red currants from the laden bushes and topped and tailed them, a job designed for little fingers.

On wet days she pulled out her single row Hohner melodeon and played jigs and reels. There was a hole in the works where the wind escaped and it was my job to pinch the hole while she played. The tops of my fingers got sore from these sessions of exuberant dragging and squeezing of the 'box'.

If these sessions were still in progress when my sister, Jeanie, called for me, we would take turns in pinching the hole and dancing on the stone floor. During these sessions black beetles darted in all directions, showing their dislike for such disturbance. The boxes of DDT she used to rid the cottage of pests seemed to make no difference.

In later years I learnt that she was married only a short time when her husband was killed in the Civil War and thus had no children of her own. What a cruel hand she had been dealt, yet she was kind and caring and shared her time and love with a small child on her way home from school.

She taught me the arts of sharing and giving, priceless gifts to a child. And, in this ever-changing world of turning tides and trading places, she again looks down on me from above.

Short Story

The Garden

By Paul McGregor

Long Island, New York

Six years after their marriage, Eric and Lizzie were moving into their first home in a council estate and they were pleasantly surprised to discover a substantial garden

MOVING INTO their new house on that chilly day in January 1957 came after a long wait for Eric and Lizzie. They had spent the first six years of their married life with Eric's parents or in upstairs digs with a nosy landlady downstairs and, with each pregnancy, the threat of eviction.

Now, having finally reached the top of the waiting list, they signed all the papers at the council offices, picked up the keys and rent-book and went to find their new home. They'd been allocated a house on a street called Murrayfield Drive.

The word 'Drive' had an elegant note to it, but Eric knew it in no way diminished his wife's resentment at moving into a council-owned, semi-detached rather than into a house of their own, even if it was on a 'Drive.'

So they exchanged few words as Lizzie pushed the pram, a tight grip on the handle, another ambition for her married life frustrated, while Eric carried their two suitcases and tried to forget he'd fallen in her esteem. Adding to his discomfort was the suit and tie he was wearing on a weekday when he'd normally be in factory overalls, but he'd worn them to make the right impression with the council officials.

The children, aged four and three, sat quietly, face to face in their high Silver Cross pram, with an infant's awareness of the adult tension around them.

The new estate was less than a quarter of a mile from the Irish Sea and Eric caught the smell of seaweed on the breeze, while the cries of the seagulls brought to mind the B&I Ferry docking at dawn at the quayside in Dublin. It was where they had met.

The air had a taste to it too - a fresh taste, suggesting exposure to the elements, something he had not felt growing up in a narrow street of terraced houses in working-class Birkenhead.

But for the urgency of finding the new house and the weight of the suitcases, he'd have gone down to the sea to ponder on the changes in his life since he'd last crossed it and had met Lizzie at a dance in the National Ballroom. Eric was prone to such reflections but, as one of six boys, he'd learned not to voice them as people only laughed at him.

What's more, there was no time to imagine what might have been. He had two young children now and a third on the way. His thoughts shifted from Dublin and the Irish Sea to the furniture they'd have to buy and the importance of not missing the rent - all that on his weekly wages of £18.

When they finally found the address that was written on the small, blue rent-book, Eric put down the suitcases and handed the key to Lizzie.

"You open it," he said.

They exchanged glances as she took the key from him, both silently acknowledging the significance of the moment, while his tender gesture prompted a brief truce in her resentment.

The door swung open for the first time and Eric fell into reflection again. As he bent to pick up the suitcases he pondered now on how often that front door would open and close over the years ahead, how many children, grandchildren perhaps, would cross that threshold, what dramas would be played out on the stage they were entering?

The children jostled him from his thoughts, jumping out of the pram to run around the echoing rooms, enjoying freedom of movement for the first time. The sound of their feet on the bare floorboards set him to calculating the cost of putting down linoleum.

Lizzie took off her coat and automatically climbed the stairs, forgetting they could now occupy the downstairs too. As he heard her footsteps echoing above his head, something gave way inside Eric. He sat down on the stairs and let flow tears of released anxiety. At last, they had a place of their own!

She found him there, the trembling in his shoulders warning her something was wrong. She'd never seen him cry before, and she'd never see him cry again, not at four more births nor at the death of his own parents. He was an unfathomable man and she knew that her questions would elicit no answers. So she stood there, her hand on his shoulder until, with simultaneous instinct, they both became aware of the silence around them.

"Where are the children?" Lizzie asked, voicing their common thought.

She ran back upstairs while Eric went into the kitchen. It was then that he saw it - through the window he caught his first sight of the long garden stretching out far behind the house.

He hadn't expected the place to have a garden and certainly not one so big. In the hyperbole of his reflections he compared the discovery to that of the Spanish explorer he'd once read about who, after fighting his way through the tropical forests of Panama, at last set sight on the Southern Sea, later known as the Pacific Ocean.

The vegetation had grown high while the house had stood empty. He spotted movement in the undergrowth, revealing the children's location.

"They're down here, Lizzie!" he shouted to his wife as he opened the back door and went out to make an initial charting of the wilderness.

He couldn't quite make out where their garden ended and the neighbour's began, but he reckoned it was close on fifty yards long and twenty across. His childhood home had been a two-up, two-down with an alleyway at the back, so he'd never envisaged anything like this. He came from a family of ships' riveters, adept at steel, not soil. He stood and stared at it all wondering how he'd manage, having never touched a spade in his life.

The children were too young ever to remember how this land was conquered. In later years they could never recall how their father had managed to replace the weeds and wild grass with a decent-looking lawn, flower-beds and rows of potatoes, carrots and beetroot.

The earliest black and white photographs taken by their mother with her Brownie box camera showed a garden already under control if not manicured. But he must have been out there night after night and at weekends, first scything through the high weeds, then digging the heavy soil, planting grass and setting aside a part of the land for vegetables.

He did once tell them that it was their uncle Bernard who had laid the path of crazy paving right to the bottom of the garden. But they had no memory of that engineering feat. For them the path had always existed, like an archaeological find uncovered at a stroke of their Dad's scythe. They were like late settlers in a land long since colonised.

Nor did they remember the day their grandfather brought the sapling that became the apple tree. For them the apple tree had always been there too. It was a reference point in their childhood geography as fixed as the South Pole.

'I'll race you to the apple tree and back,' they'd shout in their games and when asked where the dying, stray cat had ended up they'd say, 'Oh, we buried him under the apple tree,' taking morbid delight in being party to that occult knowledge.

Though they had no recollection of their father's original inroads, the boys would always remember how on Sunday afternoons, braces hanging loose off his shoulders and white cotton shirt open at the neck, he'd push the mechanical lawn mower up and down, up and down, leaving alternating strips of dark and light green lawn behind him. They'd be on call to unhook the collecting bin and carry the cut grass to the 'tip' in the far corner of the garden. Blades of grass would spill out and get lodged in their summer sandals or float in the air and land in their hair or on sweaty faces. That night, leaves of grass would even turn up stuck to the edge of the bathtub after they'd pulled the plug.

And they'd be glad when their father finished the mowing because their football game could resume. The garden would be

Goodison Park once again. The eldest would always get to be Everton and the younger would reluctantly accept to be West Ham, but never Liverpool. It was not till they were well into their teens, when homework replaced football, that grass began to thrive where the bare patches used to mark the goal-area.

For their mother, the garden was mainly somewhere she could hang out the washing while the children played.

'They're quite happy in the garden; they don't want to play out in the street with those rough ones from around the corner,' she'd tell friends and neighbours if they suggested her children were being anti-social, or worse, being isolated against their will.

For the children it was indeed where they tasted freedom from outside interference. They could be whom they wanted in the garden: the England captain scoring the winning goal against Brazil, a cowboy on the wash-house roof, defending the home from Indians who were shooting arrows from beyond the apple-tree.

It was also where they gained a perspective that they took to the world outside. Life, like their games, had rules. And seeing their father struggle to get a decent crop of potatoes, and weeds that always grew faster than flowers, they had no illusions about nature.

It was not the 'mother' spoken about by those who had only a theoretical acquaintance with it. It was more a wicked witch. The smell of freshly-cut grass brought to them memories of hard labour not of lazy summers and the 'green' delusions of their richer friends would always strike them as naive.

From the way the grass kept growing and the weeds kept spreading, they knew that if certain things in life were not kept under control all their father's civilizing efforts would be thwarted and reversed.

As they grew up and bought their own homes, the garden in Murrayfield Drive generated other gardens, as though from pollen carried on the wind, and the settlers brought what they had garnered from following the lawn-mower and from playing their games by the rules.

One day, standing at the sink, Lizzie looked out and saw Eric walking up the path, his trousers loose around his thinning waist. She told herself he was just coming in for his cup of coffee as he did every morning, in the new schedule of his retirement days. But she knew there was something amiss, something in his demeanour and a tone in his voice that she did not like. It was as though he was trying to fathom a mystery when he asked:

"Did I really do all that?"

They both looked out through the kitchen window. They saw the mowed lawn, the freshly-painted bench under the apple-tree, the flower-beds clean of weeds, and the yellow blossom on the forsythia tree.

"Of course you did, Eric, who else?" Lizzie answered, a loving tone in her voice, trying to make light of the ominous note in her husband's.

He quietly relished her affirmation, but still, in the weakness that had come with age and seeing how far it was to the bottom of the garden, Eric doubted it could possibly be true.

He died a few months later, his job done. He'd brought order to a small patch of the earth and regained his wife's esteem.

Short Story

Scorcher and the Spud

By Paul Griffin
St. Helens, Merseyside

Jack Searson had been a great racing cyclist in his day and had made many friends in the sport. In the most unexpected circumstances, he met up again with one of them

IT WAS LATE September and the nights were drawing in with a vengeance. Thunder rumbled far off in the Dublin mountains. Down in the city, in a modest terraced house off the South Circular Road, Jack Searson was having trouble reading his paper because of the gathering gloom. He finally sighed, put down his pipe and went over to the mantelpiece to light the gas.

Just then, he heard the sound of heavy hobnailed boots on the flagged pavement outside the window. There was an unmerciful banging on the front door, and the cry of: "Open in the King's name!" Jack knew only too well what this meant. It was Sergeant Watts from the nearby barracks, carrying out one of his routine searches. The sergeant was well-known, and not at all liked, in the neighbourhood.

His searches were carried out with extreme thoroughness. It was not unusual for items to go missing, particularly tobacco or small valuables. Anybody who dared to ask the reason for these visits was told, in a broad Cockney accent and in no uncertain terms, where to get off.

Jack made haste to unbar the door before the soldiers had it down, and the sergeant and his men stormed into the hallway. A couple went upstairs, while others disappeared into the rooms on the ground floor. Drawers could be heard opening and closing, none too gently. The men had left the front door open, and there was a polite knock on it. An officer entered, walking with a stick, and removed his cap. He came into the parlour where Jack was.

"Look here," he said. "I'm awfully sorry to have to disturb you like this. We'll be out of your house in a few minutes." Jack was standing in front of the piano, on which were some framed photographs. One showed a young man in a close-fitting athletic costume, holding a racing bicycle. The officer's gaze fell on this photograph, then turned to Jack, clearly the man in it, if a few years older now and somewhat heavier.

"Merciful heavens!" he exclaimed. "Scorcher Searson, if I'm not mistaken. What a small world it is. Good to see you again, Jack." Jack suddenly recognised the man who spoke to him. He extended his hand, and they shook warmly.

"Lieutenant Henderson," he said. "Although I see it's Major now."

The officer smiled. "Nothing like a war to get you promotion. Ah, sergeant," he said, as Watts came downstairs and entered the room. "You'll find nothing of interest in this house. Please take your men and conduct your search elsewhere."

"But sir," protested the sergeant. "We 'aven't been through the place properly yet."

The major spoke crisply. "Sergeant," he said. "'Make no difficulties, I beg you. I can personally vouch for this gentleman. You have your orders. Be good enough to carry them out."

With a bad grace, Sergeant Watts called his men and led them outside, where they got into a Crossley tender. Major Henderson closed the door behind them, re-entered the parlour and apologised again for the disturbance. He accepted a fill of tobacco and lit his pipe, while Jack did the same.

"So how are you these days?" asked the major. "I heard you'd given up the track. A great pity, because you were the best rider I ever came up against. Every time we met, you absolutely thrashed me. Remember Herne Hill in '08? What a meeting that was. You gave the world champion a scare that time. And I'm sure you know that your record for the mile still stands?"

Jack smiled, somewhat ruefully, and tapped his chest more or less in the region of the heart. "'The doctor gave me no choice," he said. "He told me that if I don't exert myself too much, I could live to a ripe old age. If I'd carried on riding, I probably wouldn't be here now. What about yourself? Have you ridden at all since the war ended?"

By way of reply, the officer tapped his gaitered right leg with his walking stick. The sound it made was not that of flesh and blood, but something altogether harder.

"Afraid my riding days are over too," he declared. "But I enjoyed them while they lasted. The one thing nobody can take from you is your memories, whatever else you lose. So what are you doing for a living now? I seem to remember you had a trade before you turned to cycling."

"I was a painter and decorator,"' Jack told him. "So was my old Da, and I served my time with him. Trouble is, we used to push all our ladders and tools in a heavy handcart. I couldn't do that now with the old ticker. So I work in a shop in the city, selling hats.

"It's boring sometimes, and I do miss my trade. I'd take it up again if there was some way to get around apart from the handcart, but all the quality work is miles away from here."

The two men reminisced for a while, then Major Henderson stood up, rather stiffly, and picked up his cap and stick. "I'd better be getting along," he said, "before the sergeant gets into too much mischief. I'll call again when I'm not on duty, if I may?"

Jack assured him that he would always be welcome, and saw him to the door.

A week or so passed and, true to his word, Major Henderson called again. When Jack showed him into the parlour, a cheerful fire was blazing, and a young man was sitting beside it. He rose as the officer entered the room.

"Major Henderson," said Jack. "I'd like you to meet Harry, my son." The two shook hands and the major asked Harry what he did for a living.

"I'm an apprentice cooper up at the brewery," replied Harry. "My Da always says how important it is to have a trade. I have another ambition, though, only I don't know if I'm good enough. I'd like to be a professional racing cyclist one day."

The major smiled broadly. "Well, Jack," he said. "That would be something, to have another rider in the family. How do you feel about it?"

"I could hardly stand in his way," replied Jack, "as long as he has a trade to fall back on. Cycling was a great life for me. I saw places I'd never have got to otherwise."

They passed a very pleasant evening, and it was the first of many visits the major would make to the small terraced house. It was something of a contrast to his own large place in the country, but he was always made very welcome there, and the parlour was warm and cosy.

Meanwhile, in the city and further afield momentous events were taking place. It was a time of great change. Jack and the major would often discuss the latest news, and both were slightly regretful that the world with which they were familiar seemed to be vanishing. Major Henderson told Jack that he'd enjoyed being stationed in Dublin, and would be sorry to leave.

Eventually, though, that day arrived. The garrison was stood down and everything packed up ready to be taken down to the docks, to sail away from Ireland for the last time. The major, as commanding officer, oversaw the operation and was one of the last to leave. Sergeant Watts was his driver, in the Crossley tender. Watts was fiercely proud of this vehicle, and treated it as his own personal property. Any soldier who appeared to have a few spare minutes would be ordered to wash and polish it, and it was always immaculate.

"Right, Watts," said Major Henderson. "I think that's everything taken care of. We'd better set off for the docks. I'd just like to make a small detour, to say goodbye to an old friend."

Watts took a gold watch out of his pocket, and consulted it. "But sir," he said. "I don't know as what we've got time for any detours."

The major looked intently at the watch. "May I see that?" he asked. "It's an extremely fine one. How long have you had it?"

"Why, sir, I picked it up in France," Watts said. 'I traded it with a chap for something or other, as I recall." He handed it over for the officer to look at. Henderson turned the watch over and opened the outer case. Inside was an inscription. It read: 'Presented to Jack Searson of Dublin for the fastest time in the mile, Crystal Palace, June 1912.' The colour drained from Watts' face. He'd never opened the back of the case, but now wished he had. The major pocketed the watch.

"I think we'd better see this returned to its rightful owner, don't you?" he said. "Now, be kind enough to drive me where I tell you. And I can assure you that you haven't heard the last of this."

The Crossley tender turned into the street where Jack lived. The officer got out, and seemed to pause for a few moments at the back of the vehicle, before knocking on the door and being admitted.

"Well, Jack," he said, "I'm afraid this is goodbye, for the time being at least. I'll certainly keep a look-out for your son's name, and make a point of watching him if ever he's riding over in London. Thanks for your hospitality over the last couple of years. Oh, and I nearly forgot. I think this is yours." He took out the watch and handed it over.

Jack was astonished to see it. It was always kept in a drawer, and he hadn't missed it. They said their farewells and he saw the major to the door. The officer climbed into the Crossley and instructed the sergeant to drive to the docks. But the engine flatly refused to start. The sergeant, red-faced and exhausted from swinging on the starting-handle, was confounded.

"Sir, I don't know what's wrong," he protested. "You know as what I always keep it in perfect condition. Why, I 'ad it thoroughly checked over only yesterday, ready for the journey back to Blighty."

"Well," replied Henderson, "we've no time to mess about with it now, and all the fitters have left. Look here, you'd better run to the South Circular Road and flag down another of our vehicles. Take our kit bags with you." Under a cloud as he was, the sergeant obeyed meekly. He managed to intercept one of the last lorries and instructed the driver to wait for Major Henderson. Meanwhile, the officer explained the problem to

Jack, and asked him if he'd keep an eye on the Crossley until someone came to recover it. Jack said he would, and Henderson set off on foot, giving a cheery wave as he turned the corner.

That was the last time the two men ever saw each other, but they did keep in touch. Henderson wrote shortly afterwards to tell Jack that he'd been put in charge of army equipment and vehicles in the south of England. It fell to him to account for anything which had been left behind in Ireland.

He had, of course, reported the broken-down Crossley tender, still sitting forlornly outside Jack's front door. He was told that it would be uneconomical to recover, and that he was to obtain scrap value for it. Five pounds was deemed to be a fair figure. Henderson wrote to Jack to say that, if he could send a postal order for that amount, the Crossley would be legally his and all the papers would be sent over so that he could re-register it.

The letter carried a curious postscript. It said: "Have a look in the exhaust pipe." Puzzled, Jack went outside and knelt down in the roadway behind the Crossley. How on earth had he never noticed that before? Jammed inside the exhaust pipe was a large potato.

In the years that followed the repainted Crossley tender became a familiar sight around Dublin, with "J. Searson, Painter and Decorator" expertly signwritten on the side. Jack had lost none of his skill, and soon acquired a good reputation for high-class work. As soon as he could afford it, he had a new bicycle built for Harry. Eventually, though, it was clear that, despite his keenness, Harry would never be the rider his father was. What he could be, though, was a really first-class cooper. With that, and the knowledge of what a great sportsman his father had been, he was more than content.

Memories

BLUE DIAMONDS

BY EILEEN CASEY
Old Bawn, Dublin

'Juggy' was a character around town and got her name because she was always borrowing milk; once she had the cup of 'tae', nothing else mattered, she often said.

'JUGGY' WAS A bird-like woman with a round face scrubbed to a high shine, its surface cracked with veins. They reminded me, a young girl of eight or nine, of little worms wriggling under her cheeks which were red as the lipstick my mother wore on Fridays to go shopping in the town.

'Juggy' got her name because she was always trying to borrow milk. 'A few grains of tae and sugar' were the natural accompaniments to the milk and seldom was she refused. Once she had the cup of 'tae', nothing else mattered, she often said. She must have lived off bread, butter and jam because that's all that ever seemed to peek from her shopping bag.

Whenever she went to the town, she brought home empty cardboard boxes so that her house was surely full of them. We could only guess what these boxes were for; storage, perhaps, or furniture? We imagined her few household goods and foodstuffs packed into these boxes - tins of peas or beans nestled beside threadbare tea-towels or the dull glint of cutlery.

Maybe the boxes were for security reasons? Juggy could well have been barricading herself from would-be thieves behind layers and layers of cardboard. She wore lots of layers herself, winter and summer. A headscarf always covered the wispy hair. Her coat was a dull grey gabardine tied with twine. Thick stockings and brown shoes with lace ups completed her wardrobe. We'd sometimes glimpse her floral apron underneath her coat.

It was her eyes, though, I remember most. Like blue diamonds they were, shining out of her face with life and mischief. They flashed like lightning if anyone 'riled' her but when her jug was filled with a generous measure, they bestowed a radiant glow on her benefactor.

I'd heard it said that she danced all night (heavy shoes no obstacle) at any gathering she could cadge her way into, the 'afters' at weddings being a particular favourite. Everyone would be mellow from the fine fare and didn't mind the appearance of one or two uninvited guests.

Juggy more than earned her keep by doing the rounds of the room wishing everyone well and heaping praise on the bride and groom and all belonging to them. She must have known every Irish blessing there was. "May your children and children's children never want for anything," "May the road rise up to meet you," or "The blessings of God and his Holy Mother on you...." tripped lightly off her tongue.

All the while she'd be drinking sherry, her favourite tipple and probably what contributed to those little blue veins in her cheeks. A kind neighbour usually brought her home though no-one ever got past the hallway.

Juggy went to funerals, too, trying to dim the brightness in her eyes by keeping them lowered as the coffin was wheeled down the church. Afterwards, she was like a politician in the churchyard, shaking everyone's hand.

Her real name was Chrissie; 'Juggy' behind her back, Chrissie to her face. Christina, the name of a Nordic Queen; how she came by it, or indeed anything else about her, was shrouded in mystery.

There was no family but she could have been taken from an orphanage as a young girl, like a lot of the older people around the town with no apparent history. Then, when her working life was done, she ended her days in a council house on our road. She collected old newspapers too, "for lighting the fire" she said. The full extent of her paper hoarding didn't come to light until after she passed away.

Juggy died during a particularly frosty winter, near Christmas time. Holly berries were strung like lanterns around houses which were too small to accommodate a Christmas tree. It was cold enough for snow my father said each morning when he'd come in from his rounds as a postman. All we children could think about was Santa and the hot cocoa that would be waiting for us after school.

It was a few days before it was noticed that Juggy's familiar figure, with either cardboard box or jug, was missing from the scene. Buried in a pauper's grave, there were no relatives to claim or to mourn her. But her funeral was well attended by the neighbours from the street and me. Just a little girl then, I couldn't help but wonder where all that blue light in her eyes had gone.

May the good earth be soft under you
when you rest upon it,
And may it rest easy over you when,
at the last, you lay out under it;
And may it rest so lightly over you
that your soul may be out
from under it quickly,
and up, and off,
And be on its way to God.

Short Story

Manipulated

By Skye Dawson
Drumshanbo, Co. Leitrim

Mary had been intimidated and coerced unwillingly into one of her son's criminal scams and was now trapped; she couldn't see any way out of her dreadful dilemma

SHE NEVER looked back, not once. It wasn't right, but it's what she had to do. She walked straight ahead like anyone would, anyone innocent, who had nothing to hide. Not looking back distanced her from the reality of her situation; it made it less real, like she hadn't done exactly what she had.

But not looking back could only fool her for so long, until the next person came along and it happened again. It was a spiral, she was stuck and now she certainly couldn't get out. She was way too involved now, not just physically but emotionally.

Sam wouldn't be happy with her, she knew that. She had fumbled, made a mistake with her words. "Making a mistake could ruin everything, don't make mistakes." Sam had drilled the words into her head. She knew exactly what she had to say, she had a plan. Granted, she always had to twist her words to suit a person, but she had a guideline.

She wasn't blindly going into it, saying whatever came into her mind. She felt more comfortable with having a guideline, it almost made it feel less real and she would do anything to make it feel like it wasn't happening. It was a dream, a dream that she surely had to wake up from.

She often wondered what had gone wrong. She always prided herself on being a good mother, she certainly provided for her kids, working long hard hours, trying to scrounge up the money to provide them with food and clothes. They never went to school looking less than anyone else, and she made sure of it.

When Larry died, she found it tough. Her husband was the sole provider of the house and without him they struggled. But, she always told herself, they had a house, they had food and they had warmth. What more could they need? Sure, she wasn't always there but that was only because she was out busting her backside trying to make an honest living.

She knew the people used to whisper about her, giving her pitying looks. "She leaves the kids alone all day." They'd whisper. "She's probably a prostitute." At first it stung, but she got over it. She learned quickly how to form a cold mask and block out the comments. Sometimes she questioned why she had got the particular life she lived. She was a good person, why did the good people get the hard lives?

The winter was coming soon, which meant Sam would want more from her, he always did. It was an expensive time of year. As she pottered down the road, her arms laden with bags of messages, she could feel the cold blowing through her much too thin coat. She gave almost everything she had to Sam; money, clothes, food. She kept only the bare minimum for herself, but she didn't mind. Sam needed it much more than she did.

She shrugged in her jacket, trying to preserve whatever heat was trapped inside it. As she did this, she could feel one of the plastic bags she had slung over her wrist, begin to rip. "Ah no," she mumbled to herself. Just as she stopped, about to fix the bag so it wouldn't rip any more, the plastic gave way and her messages spilled out onto the cold concrete ground. She let out a few choice words before bending down to pick up the various items.

She pulled another plastic bag from her pocket. As she did this, she spotted a pair of brown leather shoes headed her way. "Mary?" The voice called out questioningly. Mary looked up quickly from the ground and flashed the old woman a quick smile. "Ah, how'ya Cheryl?" Cheryl reached her and bent down to help her pick up the groceries.

Her grey hair was pinned back into a tight bun and she wore a long brown skirt and purple coat, "Old people clothes" as Mary called them. She'd never be caught dead in them. "I'm so glad I bumped into you, Mary. I wanted to thank you for your advice on that computer company. You were dead right, my computer's running much faster now. Thank you!" Cheryl beamed at her, her thin lips spread back, the laughter lines showing and false teeth baring.

Mary froze. She hated when they brought it up. Putting the last item into the bag, she stood up and smiled at Cheryl, though it was forced, extremely forced. "Don't mention it, Cheryl."

Cheryl opened her mouth as if to say something, but Mary had already taken two steps forward. "Better be going Cheryl. Thanks for your help." And then she scurried off, as fast as a woman could with bags of shopping, leaving a slightly confused Cheryl behind.

Mary let out a sigh as she placed the bags on her counter top. All she wanted to do was to go to sleep, but she knew she couldn't, Sam would be there soon. Almost as if someone was reading her thoughts, her front door banged open and then slammed shut.

"Ma?" Sam's voice rang out through her small house like an alarm. "In here." She called out a little shakily. She knew deep down it was wrong, very wrong to be afraid of your own son, but she couldn't help it. Sam bounded through the sitting room and into the kitchen, she had her back to him, but she could hear him place a large object on the table.

She froze, she knew exactly what it was. Turning around her eyes went straight to her grandson, who was fast asleep in his car seat. She hated when he brought him, he only did it to manipulate her, she knew it. "I was just talking to Cheryl down there, she was telling me all about how you helped her with her computer."

Sam's hair was cut short, the blonde sticking out in all directions. There were bags under his eyes, his skin was a grey colour, giving him age he certainly didn't have. He hadn't always looked like that, he used to look young and healthy. He walked towards her, stopping only when he was directly in front of her. "Good job Ma," he said.

She felt relieved, it wasn't often he was happy with her. "But, you can't talk to her much anymore. It's not good, not safe. You could make a mistake." She tried her best not to let her face fall. Cheryl was her friend, she couldn't afford to lose any more friends.

"But Sam, she's my good friend. I don't want to ..." She tried to protest, but he didn't let her, he never let her. "Ma, I said you couldn't. This is serious, okay? You can't just talk to anyone you damn well like." His voice was rising, that was never a good sign. He took a step closer to her, his face mere inches from hers. "You got that, yeah?" She nodded her head; there was no use in arguing. There never was, she could still feel the sting of the slap from the last time she had.

She made them both a cup of tea and they sat down in the sitting room. "Okay, so how many this week?" Sam didn't touch his tea, but kept his eyes on his mother. She thought for a second. She had Maggie on Monday, Cheryl on Wednesday and Beatrice that day. "Three." She told him confidently. It was a good number, not too many, not too little.

Sam nodded, happy with her answer. "Good, good. What did you tell them? I want to know exactly, the boss is coming down hard on me this week." Mary let out a quiet sigh, she didn't want to relive the moments. She did her job and she did it well. Why did she have to think back on the times that she deceived her friends?

"Sam, come on, it's the same as always ..." He didn't let her finish. "Ma? Did you not hear me? The boss is coming down hard. Do you want me to lose my job?" His eyes flashed to his sleeping son. "Do you want Bobby to live in poverty?"

Mary shook her head and sighed again. "Okay, well firstly I told them that my computer was running slow and that I had rung a company and they had fixed it for me." Sam nodded and indicated for her to continue. She took a deep breath and clenched her fists. "I convinced them that if their computer broke, that the phone would break and the TV."

Sam let out a small laugh and shook his head. She continued. "I told them how easy it was, what they had to do - call, log in on the website - and then I gave them the number. Then I left." She kept her eyes fixed on the floor, she hated herself, she was worthless.

"And the old bats won't even know what hit them, a hundred euros here and there, sure they'll never notice." Sam sat back and laughed, he was doing well for himself ever since he landed the job and bringing his mother in on it only lessened his workload.

After Sam left, Mary couldn't find it in herself to relax. She always felt this way after one of his visits. He shook every fiber in her being, he ruined her. She sat on the couch in complete silence, staring at the blank wall in front of her. She could remember clearly the day Sam had landed his 'job' like it was only the day before, not over a year ago.

She was pottering about her house, cleaning things that didn't need to be cleaned, listening to Joe Duffy on the radio. Her kids were grown up and she got her pension so she hadn't much to do. Admittedly, she was a little bored but she didn't really mind, it was better than being so busy you almost collapsed from exhaustion.

She hadn't seen her eldest son, John, in a long time. He had moved off far away to Cork with his wife, a woman she never particularly liked, and hardly ever found time to call, let alone visit. Sam lived down the road, but he was always getting into trouble, she had come to a point where sometimes she didn't want anything to do with him.

So, when he knocked at her door, you can understand why she was a little surprised. "Sam?" she asked, a little bewildered. Sam pushed past her and walked straight into the kitchen. Mary closed the door and followed him in. He was pacing around the room, hand scratching the back of his neck. He was nervous, scared, anxious. She could see it, it was written all over him.

"Sam? What's wrong?" Sam stopped pacing and pulled his hand down his face. "I got a girl pregnant." He said, his voice low. Mary drew in a sharp breath. She knew he was in no position to be a father. He had no job, no career, nothing. "She's keeping it and she said she's going to sue if I don't support."

Mary closed her eyes and blew out slowly through her nose. She was disappointed for so many reasons, she felt like a failure. She had failed in raising her child correctly. She couldn't think of anything to say. It seemed cruel but she couldn't hide the fact that she felt no emotion towards the man standing in front of her, she barely recognised him.

"What about money?" It was all she could think of. Sam perked up a little and stopped pacing. "I have a job lined up. It's why I'm here, I need your help."

She narrowed her eyes at him. Why would he need her help? "Sam, if this has anything to do with drugs, I'm not helping you." Sam shook his head furiously. "No, it's not drugs. It's something completely different."

And so he explained it to her. He was a scammer, a hacker, what ever you wanted to call it. People rang up looking for help with their computers, they logged into a website and suddenly he had complete access to everything on the computer; credit card numbers, accounts, passwords, everything. It was low, sneaky and manipulative.

She didn't agree with him doing it but she didn't complain either. She couldn't understand what that had to do with her, but Sam soon explained. In order for the company to work, people had to ring up, that's where she came in. Sam wanted her to convince people she knew to ring the number. Their main target was old people, people who didn't understand technology.

They wouldn't know what they were doing and plus, they wouldn't notice a few hundred disappearing from their accounts every now and again. It was the perfect plan. Of course at first she refused. She wanted nothing to do with Sam and his schemes. That was the first time he hit her. She had never been hit violently before but it was the first of many. Sam used anyway he could to get to her; emotional blackmail, mental and physical abuse.

He manipulated and tormented her until she couldn't protest anymore, but did what he asked. She tried to tell John but he was incredibly hard to get a hold of and even when she finally got in touch, she couldn't bring herself to tell him. Mary wiped a tear from her eyes as she relived the memory. She'd never forget it as long as she lived.

She didn't hear from Sam the rest of the week, which wasn't unusual. She usually only heard from him once a week, just so he could check up on her. She continued with her job like she always did, convincing innocent people to ring the god forsaken company. It wasn't until Wednesday that she heard from anyone.

She got up from the couch where she was absentmindedly watching the television to answer the door. It was quite late in the evening, so she was a little surprised to hear from anyone. She slowly opened the door, not knowing who to expect to see. Sam stood in the doorway, physically shaking. He barged passed her and ran into the kitchen.

She couldn't shake the feeling of deja-vu. "It's the Guards, Ma. They're after me. The company's gone bust, we're in it deep Ma, we're in it deep." He paced around the room, continuously scratching his neck. Another knock at the door caused them to lock eyes. Mary felt a shiver run through her, this was it. Sam ran towards her, begging for her not to answer but she walked straight to the door and flung it open.

Two Guards stood in her doorway. "Excuse me mam, is this Mary Murphy's house?" Mary looked up at the tall male Garda and nervously nodded her head. This was it. "Mam, we're looking for Sam Murphy. Do you know his whereabouts?" Mary took a deep breath and stood back. She had to do it, if it was the last thing she did. "In here."

She lay on her bed and sighed. She was free. No more manipulation, no more blackmail, nothing. She was finally free. She lay there staring up at the white ceiling until her eyes slowly closed. Whether they'd open again, she didn't know. She didn't care, she was free.

Memories

The Worst Boy in the School

By Vincent J. Doherty
Palmer's Green, London

Schooling was much less formal in the 1950s, with huge classes and very flexible notions on curriculum and time time-tables, but somehow the dedicated teachers managed to impart some knowledge and some lessons for life

THERE WERE 59 of us in our class at Barrack Street Boys in the 1950s. We jostled elbow to elbow on hard wooden forms, row after row behind well-worn desks and learnt as best we could, or wanted to, from dedicated schoolmasters who taught us in their own ways with whatever materials they had to hand.

If there was a National curriculum, or any other kind of curriculum, we were never aware of it and if there were inspectors they never dared to come near us. Days began with Master Carroll pulling a crumpled newspaper out of his pocket, detailing the lives and deaths of great men and tyrants, of disasters and natural wonders, creating a lesson that might last an hour or all day.

We learnt our geography by rote; the rivers of Australia, the Prairie Provinces, with the help of a never ending supply of 'The National Geographic'. We learnt handwriting, scratching compositions with rusty nibs in ancient pens on rough jotters.

History was the wolf feeding Romulus and Remus, Horatius defending a bridge, Napoleon on the road to Moscow and the evil English chasing the Earls out of Ireland. We learnt to roar 'The Minstrel Boy' and 'The Harp that once...' conducted with the aid of a tuning fork. On quieter days we bellowed 'Oft in the stilly night' and prepared to recite 'Young Lochinvar' who came out of the West, for the Parish carnival.

For art, we dug potato prints and gouged lino cuts and the careless gouged themselves. Mental arithmetic in those days before calculators meant cowering in the headmaster's classroom hoping we wouldn't be questioned and often shedding tears when we were, as he fired question after question in our direction:

"Eight fives, McCusker?"

"Forty, sir.

"Nine threes, McGarrigle?"

"Er - twenty four sir."

A slap of the strap and McGarrigle knew what nine threes were from that day forward. We often finished those lessons with hot hurting hands and a solid grounding in the discipline of mathematics.

We never seemed to be bound by any timetable. Routine could be set aside for days or weeks at will. The month before Confirmation meant catechism, nine till three, Monday to Friday. When Master Foley acquired a 'Book of Kells' one summer, we spent three weeks designing or destroying Celtic letters with varying degrees of artistry, accuracy and rarely accomplishment.

There were occasional visitors, the most memorable of them being Fernie the Magician who arrived on a motorbike and produced rabbits out of his helmet. He was also the World draughts champion, he claimed; a man to be admired.

There were film shows after school in St. Patrick's Hall where for a thrupenny bit in aid of the School Building Fund we could watch Rob Roy McGregor, Long John Silver or Robin Hood, swashbuckling across the bed sheet which stood in for a screen. When restless boys dodged behind that screen their shadows loomed large with the swashbucklers, adding to the excitement, action and appreciation.

Summer afternoons sometimes meant football in the Parochial Field, with coats for goalposts, charging about like young bullocks let out to grass. On other days a master might organise boxing in the cindered yard at the back of the school. We would make a 'ring' with forms from our classroom and yell our heads off as 'gladiators' laid into one another with more enthusiasm than skill.

Scrapping wasn't confined to the 'ring'. Many exchanges

of opinions begun at playtime reached their natural conclusion after school, along the Main Street and down the Water Wall. In those days before daytime television such events provided live entertainment for the whole town, hundreds of tutting and appreciative spectators stopping any traffic in its tracks. In my time I played an active role in many of those entertainments. After one such occasion when I arrived home my mother, convinced she was rearing a potential genius, asked her usual, "What did you do in school today?" Rather than regale her with glad tidings of academic excellence, I complained that some boys were picking on me and I'd had to fight them.

The next morning she was waiting for the headmaster outside his office. "There are bullies in this school picking on my wee boy," she started. The great man asked my name. She told him. His retort was short and to the point. "Missus, your wee boy is the worst boy in the school."Her instruction to me that evening was equally short and to the point; "Bring me a rod."

We were a motley crowd but we got an education and we ended up in all kinds of jobs all over the world, building skyscrapers, digging motorways and policing the streets. And 'The worst boy in the school' became a schoolmaster!

Short Story

Everything in its Place

By Paul McLaughlin
Belfast

Paddy at last has time to reflect after all the fussing surrounding his wife's funeral following her death in a car accident, and eventually he turns with anticipation to Gillian's last will and testament ...

BACK AT THE HOUSE, I breathed heavily, relieved that it was over. The previous three days had little time left to think, although I felt like I had been in the front row of a scrum of sympathy. Sudden bereavement brings its own distinctive bruising.

I drew the Regency-striped curtains and watched as an anaemic April sun struggled to light up the room. All was neatly in place, as always. The Chesterfield stood solemnly against the wall facing the bay window. It looked a little forlorn now, missing its companion I supposed. The other large sofa, the "twins" as Gillian used to call them, had been removed on Monday night to make room for her coffin.

The cast-iron fireplace, with its high mantel and inlay of mosaic tiles, flanked it like a solid friend and, for the first time that I could remember, a thin veneer of dust covered it. That would have been given short shrift if Gillian had been here.

She had always been a stickler for tidiness. Dusting had made way for vacuuming and polishing on a daily basis that had irritated while it eradicated. Scatter cushions were beaten within an inch of their existence before being scattered equidistantly apart. I had watched this on several occasions; on those dreadful days when it had been too wet to go golfing and that interminable month when I had had an ankle encased in plaster.

"Everything in its place and a place for everything" she would say. Ten thousand times she must have said it, as what at first had seemed an endearing idiosyncrasy had developed into a maddening mantra.

I sat back in Granny Megahey's old armchair, Gillian's grandmother of course. "How was it that nothing of my family had managed to pass our home entrance exam?" I heard myself speak aloud again for only the second time in as many hours. The sound of my voice made me smile. There you go, she's dead and we are still arguing.

I lay back and put my feet up on the embroidered footstool, a pristine piece of furniture that belied its name; for it had not felt the heel or sole of a foot in all its fifteen years. I took great pleasure in rubbing my muddy brogues against it like a marauding tom cat.

Three days since the phone call, a call that had changed everything and rectified nothing. Isn't that often the case? Things had been easier since I'd moved out of the matrimonial home, but now I was back to square one, back in the bosom of our family, Granny Megahey and all.

Even Elizabeth, especially Elizabeth, my only daughter, had been kept unaware of my earlier departure. Gillian had adhered to all the formalities. "No one must know that we have had a little difficulty," she had said.

Good Lord! 'A little difficulty'. I had been researching an annulment during my frequent absences. That's how serious I was. I'd wanted to escape from her so badly that I would've faced searchlights, machine guns and German Shepherds to get away from that voice.

"Do this, Patrick, don't do that, Patrick. A gentleman always does it like this, Patrick," as her chirping chipped away at my soul.

Once upon a time I had been Paddy Kelly from the Falls Road; tall, slim, not bad looking at all with 'a fine nose that'll never want for shortage of breath,' according to Brother Nolan at school. Paddy, who was doing awfully well at the Ulster Bank after an accountancy degree at the Queen's University, don't you know. Paddy, who had been transmogrified into Patrick after meeting Gillian at the Students' Union.

Paddy, who hadn't been back to the Falls since the deaths of his "oh so proud" mother and father; Paddy, the bit of a boy, who had the shock of chestnut, curly hair described by Gillian as "wild Fenian wool". Paddy who kept his siblings, nine sisters and a beloved twin brother, at a safe distance on his Christmas card list, from which they had been welcomed onto our mantelpiece but nowhere else; Patrick,who hadn't been to Mass for years.

"No-one must know about our little blip," Gillian had insisted: "Least said, soonest mended. I'm due for President of the Ladies' section of the golf club in March and even the teeniest whiff of scandal and I'll be scuppered."

Her accent had been on diplomacy. Gillian's Uncle Edgar had been in the Colonial Service in Burma before the war and, somehow, 'Magill Sahib', as he still referred to himself on occasion, had left a legacy of near regal behaviour.

All those little phrases that had enchanted me during our six month courtship, all the little middle class musings, with every "ing" wrung out for all it was worth, had spelt division and, worse still, its sleeping partner, resentment, before the bill for the Belfast Castle reception had been paid.

Less than a month after our volcanic fortnight in Tenerife, I'd told her in a drunken roar that Uncle Edgar "had beaten darkies for a living and a damn good living at that". On our first Christmas as a mixed marriage couple, I'd slugged seven eighths of Daddy's best Scotch, the one kept for display purposes only, and collapsed on Auntie Violet's ample bosom during a raucous rendition of Roddy McCorley.

The same bosom had got a mention earlier that evening, or so I was informed by a chastening Gillian during the Boxing Day post-mortem, but her recounting of the "disgusting" words I had used had only made me laugh like a crow, despite a raging hangover.

Of course, I had left home discreetly, by instalments you might say, so typical of a banker. An overnight bag was replenished on at least a dozen occasions to avoid the prying eyes of concerned neighbours and, eventually, I had accumulated a considerable portion of my belongings in a two-bedroom apartment that fronted the better bank of the river Lagan, if such a feature actually exists.

Elizabeth, at "Uni' as Gillian insisted on calling it, in Edinburgh, had known nothing of the split and the entire Magill and Megahey dynasties had remained safe in their ignorance; until that phone call.

Trevor Magill, Director of Major Accounts at the bank, had called me at work. In a rare show of emotion from a man reared on rugby and statistics, he'd managed, through dignified sniffles, to explain that his darling sister had been involved in a serious car accident, was seriously ill in the Ulster Hospital and, eventually, in a gush of phlegm, that she was dead. The dreaded word had escaped like a wish-less genie.

I know I had never wished her dead. I had often thought it would, perhaps, be better if she wasn't around, but not dead, not ever dead. Okay, in a thousand regret-filled nights, I may have prayed that she would pass out of my life – but not by being dead, not by passing on.

Death was for old people and sick people and other people. Not big, lively Gillian with the horsey grin and the bale of hair. I'd only wished her dead in the way you wish for a little something extra in your pay packet, for that special present at Christmas, for inconvenient things to go away. But like my mother used to say, you have to be careful what you wish for in this life.

Everybody could see that I was truly shocked and saddened by her death. The young Church of Ireland curate from St Bart's, all high church and low mileage in the job, had quoted from the Bible to fill in the gaps in his life experience and his ineptitude had proved the perfect cover for a grieving husband who really didn't know what to say.

Elizabeth, hot-foot from Prestwick airport, had looked jaded and distraught, but her natural reserve had held up and there had been none of that octopus hugging and kissing that I had witnessed and winced at as my parents were waked from this world.

Everything had been neat and tidy. The figures in the funeral set had been taken out of the box for the day, played their parts beautifully and been put away with the Protestant amens.

"Things are going to be difficult from now on," I began talking to myself, the way I always did when faced with a problem. "I've taken a 12 month lease on the apartment, but I've now got the house to myself. Elizabeth won't be home again until June and everyone will expect me to be here all the time. The one time I need that blessed woman to be here to make excuses and... aah well."

I went to the bureau in the corner of the room, a fine piece of Victoriana left to Gillian by some other scion of the Megaheys, and began the onerous task of putting my late wife's affairs in order.

"Thank God for an organised woman," I said aloud as I discovered that all the relevant material had been filed in alphabetical order and cross-referenced for easy access. "The suddenness of an avalanche couldn't have caught that girl on the wrong foot," I laughed when I thought of her and felt just a little twinge of something or other.

The will was first and foremost in my mind, but I found myself thinking fondly of the woman who had shared her life with me. The irony of the moment was not lost on me, as I fingered her signature gently on the embossed wedding album in the small, middle drawer of the bureau; a name in relief, a little milestone on life's journey?

Gillian had been a wealthy woman in her own right and I eyed the thick manila envelope eagerly. Her last will and testament and a letter addressed to me, Patrick Kelly Esquire, copied to Mr. John Glover, Solicitor.

"God Bless you, Gilly," and I found myself using the diminutive of her name for the first time in donkeys years. I ripped open the flimsy packaging and read slowly, wanting to savour every word, enjoy the acquisition of every artifact of Unionist pruck.

"*Dearest Patrick,*" it read; "*Sorry about the melodrama of this missive.*" Everybody else writes a letter, not my Gillian. I continued to read, annoyed at being irritated, but expectant all the same.

"Patrick, I'll try to keep this as short and to the point as possible.

I have tolerated your infidelities for longer than I care to remember. I turned a blind eye to such hurt because I loved you and I did not want to disrupt our life together. I was foolish and old-fashioned enough to believe that you would grow out of it. But, then, my naiveté was what attracted you to me in the first place, Well, that and the money of course.

"I have instructed my solicitor to execute my will. In short, Elizabeth inherits everything, the money, the house and the land. The lot! Goodness, how I wish that I could see your face at this moment, darling Patrick. It must be a picture."

I found my hands shaking as my reflection in the over-mantle bore out her words, but I read on.

"To you my dearest Paddy, for it is Paddy that you were always, no matter how hard I tried to change you, I leave all my love and heartfelt prayers that you will be happy without me. Unfortunately, I could never be happy without you.

"I know I could not share your impish sense of humour, but to paraphrase you when you mocked and imitated me so often; 'There is a place for everything and everything is now in its place'."

I sat for a long time watching the first buds of the year stand out a proud Irish green against foliage of burnt Ulster orange before I spoke to the window: "No sense of humour indeed! What a woman! It might be a good time to ring the brother."

Memories

Aunt Ginny's Holdall

By Mary Sheil

Drumcondra, Dublin

The mystery of the contents of Aunt Ginny's precious bag was finally revealed, but in a manner that brought only regret and heartbreak

AUNT GINNY was Dad's aunt, and the nearest thing we had to a granny on that side of the family, the genuine article having died before any of us were born. She was the spitting image of one of Jimmy O'Dea's little oul Dublin biddies, down to the squashed black hat and the venerable holdall.

This fashion accessory never left her sight; before she accepted a cup of tea in our kitchen, it was placed carefully beside the leg of her chair, where it could be retrieved instantly at the slightest hint of an alarm. Whenever Aunt Ginny needed to get something out of the bag, she opened it just wide enough to insert her hand and thereafter worked by touch.

We speculated endlessly about its contents; valuables surely, to merit such unceasing vigilance, a silver teapot perhaps, priceless jewellery showered on her by a rich admirer in the days of her youth? The possibilities were endless, but seemed destined to remain a mystery.

One thing was certain though, if Aunt Ginny ***had*** anything worth selling in her holdall, she didn't intend to make use of it to improve her lifestyle. Her tiny widow's pension barely kept herself and poor Tom, as she invariably called her layabout son. He never earned a penny that we could see and he would disappear mysteriously from time to time.

"Gone to England to look for work," Aunt Ginny would say when we enquired, but Dad thought otherwise. "More likely having an all expenses paid holiday in Mountjoy jail," was his opinion. During such absences Dad went to see his aunt every week, and played along with the fiction that Tom would soon find a good job in England, where he'd get the chance denied him in Dublin.

"I could murder that no good cousin of mine," he'd explode when he got home. "He's slowly breaking his mother's heart, no matter how she tries to hide it. All he's ever done is take, take, take, and yet you know, she'd still give him her last bob."

Aunt Ginny was on familiar terms with all the delivery men who frequented our neighbourhood, and often made use of them to carry messages to us. One such note, brought by the coalman, and so smudged with coal dust as to be almost unreadable, made Dad hurry off without finishing his dinner.

He found Aunt Ginny huddled beside the unlit fire in her bare little flat, her clothes and hair awry, clutching the precious holdall, now gaping open and obviously empty.

"It's Tom," she whispered, and after Dad had made her hot sweet tea, he drew the story from her, bit by painful bit.

Tom had come home the night before, drunker than usual and spoiling for a fight. He tripped over the bag as he fell into a chair, grabbed it and turned it out onto the floor. All her treasures, the things she had tried to keep safe, were exposed to his violence, including some family photos, letters from her long dead husband, her own First Communion prayer book, and were trampled and destroyed before her eyes.

He had finally broken the last little piece of her spirit before disappearing out of all our lives.

Poor darling Ginny – at last we knew the sad truth of her precious holdall. With the same fervour with which we had once wanted to know, we now wished we had never found out.

Dad insisted she come to live with us after that, but she hadn't the heart for anything more, and nine months later we laid her gently beside her dear Michael. Tom was untraceable, then and for ever afterwards.

Short Story

Two favours

By Jacinta Lowndes
Swords, Co. Dublin

Peter was at his own wake, observing his widow and all his friends, neighbours and workmates who had gathered to see him off, amused by some of their observations. Peter had made careful preparations for this day

THE ROOM was full of fresh air. The air that says it's the end of summer and winter is on the way. The faint smell of the last of summer roses drifted in from the front hall way. There was no fire lit nor was the heat on so that with each visitor a draft of evening time glided in the doors.

The sitting room was full of women with their best clothes on, sets of pearls and glasses of sherry in their hands. The men crowded into the kitchen, close to the fridge and the back door, glasses of stout, beer or a drop of something stronger keeping them topped up. The table was laid out with plates of sandwiches, scones and apple tarts.

Peggy shook hands and acknowledged the kind words. The women agreed her husband was the best he had looked in years.

"He's like a young lad," said Mrs Shannon.

"Oh yes," agreed Francis from down the road, "and the suit, it's lovely Peggy, where did you get it?"

"Oh, he went off one day and bought that, said nothing to me, the devil. Couldn't believe it when I seen it, brought me for dinner to that new Chinese in town a few weeks ago and wore it. Surely I nearly died meself when I seen him coming down the stairs all geared up" she laughed quietly.

Peter smiled when he heard her comment, they had had a lovely meal that night, reminded them of the first time they ever went to a restaurant thirty odd years ago. They had held hands going and coming home, just like they did when they were courting.

"Is it another woman you're going out with tonight?" she had asked.

"Be God it's not, sure amn't I stuck with you, and who else would have me?"

He bet money she was remembering that moment, he watched her face, her eyes far away lost in thought, and a faint smile passed her lips. He reached out to touch her hand but the front door bell rang and she walked out to open it.

He remembered the day he had bought it. It was a stunning day in July - sunshine, blue skies, the kind of day that made you glad to be alive.

Peter Green shut the front door gently and walked down his gravel path. A gentle crunch underneath his feet echoed in the stillness of the summer day.

"I must cut that bush back," he had thought as he unlatched the front gate. The large pink hydrangea heads were brushing against him as he passed. He noticed bees hovering over the petals and landing intermittently on the delicate cerise flowers, collecting pollen for their Queen.

He wondered how it ever came to be in his garden, he couldn't remember if it was there when they moved in or had his wife planted it ages ago. They were native to South Asia; he remembered that from one of those BBC2 gardening programmes; all the way from South Asia to North Dublin.

A spider's web with a collection of flies and insects caught in its silken threads spun from dark green leaves to the metal work of the gate. The spider sat centre stage of his intricacies, a morning's work. Peter apologised to him for breaking the strands as he opened the gate.

"You've plenty of time to start again," he whispered as he bent to smell the flowers. He'd never done that before and he wondered why not. They had been there so long, blooming every summer, he walked past them twice a day at least and yet had never really paid any heed.

Was this mindfulness? The new fad they all seemed to be talking about on the radio? Perhaps.

They smelt of summer, of hot July days, of kids bare legged

playing on the road, of ice cream, of bright evenings, and most of all they smelt of his life. He sniffed again, this time closing his eyes. Mm they smelt of his summer.

He gently closed the gate and headed into town. The drapery shop he was going to was in Main Street, past the Post Office which had a queue of young people outside, collecting their dole, he guessed. "Desperate," he thought. When he was young there always seemed to be a job, doing something, anything. He used to pick scallions, spuds, carrots then drive them into the market. Pay his Ma the housekeeping every week before anything else.

When he was getting married he got the job in the factory, thirty eight years he worked there. Didn't always love it but sure it was a job; paid the bills, put the kids through school, summer holidays. He wondered when it had all changed.

Walking into the drapery he was greeted by Mr Byrne and the tingle of a bell overhead.

"Peter, there's a surprise, how are you?"

Mr Byrne had inherited the shop from his father, and it had been his grandfather's before him. It had clothed many a child for their communion, confirmation, debs, indeed, all occasions. And it had dressed Peter from the time he was knee high. There was a slight musty smell that old shops tend to have, as if there was a ghost of times past skulking on the shelves and in the corners. As the door closed behind Peter the sunshine disappeared and a shiver went down his back.

"I'm good, not a bother, no use in complaining, sure no-one listens."

"True, what can I do for you today, Peter?"

"I'm looking for a complete rig-out – a suit, shirt and tie."

"Special occasion?"

"Well, I've an important meeting coming up."

"Ah, I see, is it the Mayor or the Pope?"

"I wish. I was thinking of a navy suit and a good white shirt."

"That's no problem and the tie – what colour? Maybe pale blue?"

"It's not the guards I'm joining; no I want a pink tie, dark pink. I think the women call it cerise"

"Lovely. Lovely, I have just the one. You sit down there and I'll get a few suits out for you to try. How's all the family?"

Peter sat on the antique wooden chair and it leaned to the left as if all his weight was reliant on the front leg. He glanced around at the stock of clothes to suit all ages and sizes. He remembered sitting on the same chair, his legs dangling not even hitting the floor, when his mother was choosing his communion suit.

"They're grand. All working away, making their way in life. Good and healthy. Sure what more could you ask for. And your gang, how are they?"

"They're grand, making their millions in Canada. I'll just get one more from the back, someone asked me to keep it aside but we'll try it anyway."

Within the hour, they had tried and fitted suits, chosen the perfect one, completed it with a shirt and tie that looked elegant and smart and they had put the world to rights as they did it.

Peter looked in the full length mirror and liked what he saw.

"Well now Peter, you'd win an election in that."

Peter laughed, "I'd probably do a better job. Now would you do me a favour? Well, two favours?"

"I will if I can."

"Will you take a photo of me on me phone, I want to send it to Liz in Sydney. She won't be home till Christmas and I'd like to let her see that her auld Dad still looks good."

Mr. Byrne took a few photos and handed the phone back.

"Thanks, isn't technology great, imagine its gone all the way to Australia, amazing."

"Ah listen sure it's hard to keep up. What's the second favour Peter?"

Goosebumps rose on Peters arms and again he shivered.

"Well, I was wondering if you'd dress me for the meeting, I want to look right, tie straight and all. And you're particular and you'd know the way it should look. I know it's a funny request, it's just, well, it is an important meeting."

"Janey, that's a funny one alright, but I won't deny you. I'll put it in the diary? When is the meeting?"

"In about a month's time."

"Grand, what date?"

"You'll have to ask God that and if he tells you, don't tell me," Peter laughed the words out, as he loosened the tie.

"What are you talking about Peter?" Mr Byrne turned and watched Peter and sudden realisation drifted over him. "Ah Peter no, tell me it's not what I think it is?"

"Well sure we all have to go sometime; two certainties, death and taxes, don't you know?"

"Do you mind me asking what it is? Is it cancer?"

"It is, and it's spreading; there's not a lot they can do, so I'm just going to enjoy the last few weeks or months."

"Well, what do the doctors say, what time line like?"

"Ah sure they haven't a clue, none of us do, but I reckon I'll be lucky to see Christmas."

"Ah God, that's desperate news, and you look great. That's a shocker. What does Peggy say, how's she coping?"

"Ah sure what can she say or do, we just make the most of every day now; do normal things, even had a row last night over the feckin bins – I lost!"

"Anyway, won't you do that for me, dress me like, I want her to be proud of me."

Mr Byrne firmly placed his hand on Peter's shoulder; "It would be an honour." He felt saltiness in his eyes and strode behind the counter to open the receipt book. "Now go and change and I will hang it properly in a suit bag."

Peter went into the changing room, it seemed so tiny now in comparison to when he was a boy. The mirror was spotless, bar the little dusts of rust on it that old mirrors get.

Now, he watched in the sitting room mirror; his wife, now his widow, was being consoled by all their friends and neighbours and his old work friends. He could see the body laid out, his mother's rosary bead in his hands, the piece of palm and holy water on the white lace table cloth beside it. The only heat in the room was from the candles lit either side of a statue of Our Lady. It was a strange sensation to be able to see it and yet not be sad.

His last words to Peggy where "Go and "buy yourself new shoes." She laughed at him; "New shoes! Where are you going Peter?" But he had sent her into town to get them. While she was gone he rang Liz, chatted to her about work and the weather. He told her to mind herself in the sun – "remember how you got burnt in the Irish sun in Tramore that summer, love" and he would see her soon. He hung up and sat in his chair and said goodbye to the world he knew.

Peggy put her hands to her face and started to cry, huge tears flowed down her face. Peter looked from beyond the veil, what was it that brought this rush of emotion. A suit case fell to the floor in the hall and his beautiful daughter walked in, rushed to her mother's arms and cried, wailed the same as when she was six and had a broken arm. The room fell silent in utter grief, hearts breaking watching this family reunion.

Peter closed his eyes and hugged them both, whispering how much he loved them.

"Please, please don't be sad, I'm here," he whispered. A white feather fell to the rug where they stood crying and both looked over their shoulder, feeling his presence, and whispered to each other "I love you too, Da."

Short Story

The Castle

By Richard Cahill
Cahir, Co. Tipperary

Various plans were mooted over the years for the old castle near the village but it was eventually blown up by some local activists and the explosion also blasted apart some memories and dreams

I WAS CYCLING past Foleys' house when the explosion went off. I was on my way home from the Mercy Convent where I was a sixth year student at the time. It is imprinted on my brain forever, the sudden heart-stopping, thunderous reverberation; then the slow-motion realisation of what had just happened.

I have no recollection of dismounting from my bike, but Mrs Foley's kindly old face appeared through my tears of shock and outrage. She'd been in her front garden, dead-heading roses, red and white ones in a semi-circular bed. As the old woman took my hand and led me up the little path to her front door, the red of her roses seemed to bleed into the white.

"I never thought they'd do it, the scoundrels. They're fit for anything, but I never thought they'd blow up that beautiful castle," Mrs. Foley said, setting out tea and scones on a little glass-topped table. Her kitchen, warmed as much by its owner's hospitality as its big open hearth, was a welcome respite from the biting east wind of that mid-March evening. But as I sat there, in the bleak, unalterable knowledge of what had just happened, I was filled with a numbing dread. Everything had changed now; there could be no going back.

"Just because the aristocracy were associated with it, they had to go and destroy it," Mrs Foley fumed as she poured the tea; "blow up one of the finest buildings in the country. Philistines, that's what they are."

I wasn't sure what a philistine was but I knew she didn't intend it as a compliment. I was aware too that if I didn't get a move on, my parents would be getting anxious and Mother would soon insist on my father coming against me in the car.

But Mrs Foley's kitchen was warm and cosy and in my host I sensed an affinity and understanding I could not resist. My parents were hard working, practical people who would be less than sympathetic to my outrage over what had been done to the castle.

Now that various plans half-heartedly put forward over the years for its conversion to an hotel, an agricultural college or even a university had come to naught, the way was open for the Land Commission to divide its more than one thousand acres of fine fertile land among the local farmers, including my father.

Mrs Foley poured more tea and nudged another scone onto my plate. I sat there in front of her warming fire, responding to her mix of denunciation and gossip without really hearing her, allowing myself to drift off to a secret place in my head, a place that now no longer existed. And into that secret place, too, though I tried hard to keep him out, came Gerry.

A year or two older than me, Gerry lived in a cottage fifty yards up the road from our house. He was one of a family of thirteen; "breeding like rabbits" as my father sometimes remarked, his disapproval clear and no doubt intended as a warning to me that I should have nothing to do with any of them.

But on a road inhabited, apart from ourselves and Gerry's family, by an assortment of tetchy (as we youngsters saw them, at any rate) old spinsters and bachelors, who else was there for my brothers and I to tag around with? Tensions were heightened when my parents discovered that Gerry and I had been seen slipping off on our own through a gap in the high stone wall encompassing the estate.

There were ructions, to put it mildly. I was told in no uncertain terms that I was asking for trouble if I didn't keep away from him, and that if anything happened to me, not to come running to them.

Although we were all pretty innocent back then, I was old enough to understand what was being implied. However, my parent's disapproval of Gerry seemed only to reinforce my determination to be with him; instead of doing what I was told and ending my friendship with him (in truth, at that stage, the 'relationship' between us was no more that of a couple of kids who liked hanging around together), I now began to see Gerry in a rather different light. A seed had been planted which would lead us to become, for a little while at least, quite a bit more than simply friends.

"I heard they'd a buyer got for it an' all, Lord something or other from the north of England. He was going to do the whole place up, restore it to its former glory." Mrs Foley's increasingly angry words from time to time intruded. "But the Council still kept cutting down the trees and selling off the timber. Sure what lord, or lady for that matter, would put up with the likes of that?"

Mention of lords and ladies was another twist of the knife in my heart. It reminded me of the titles we'd taken to giving each other whenever we managed to sneak off together to the castle. Pushing up one of the heavy sash windows that opened into the servants quarters at the rear, Gerry, touching my fingers to his lips, would say: "You first, my Lady."

"Thank you, my Lord," I'd laugh, catching the hem of my mini-skirt and executing what I thought was a graceful bow.

What followed next, as I clambered through the narrow opening, would be less than graceful: Gerry pushing me from behind, my squeals of protest and laughter a dead giveaway to Jimmy the caretaker if he happened to be nearby.

Once inside though, we were safe enough. Jimmy, full of arthritis, moved slowly, content mainly to pass his days limping at snail's pace around the perimeter. Only rarely did he bother to go inside and, on the odd occasion he took it into his head to do so, never ventured beyond the first floor. Climbing the great sweeping stairway to the grand rooms above would have been next to impossible for Jimmy, whose father and his father before him had given their working lives on the estate.

Sometimes, from a high window, we'd spot him below, bundled up, rain or shine, in his heavy gabardine coat, hobbling along. Gerry made a game of throwing pieces of loose mortar from the old walls down onto the gravel behind him, and we'd double up with laughter at the startled little jump Jimmy would give, before continuing on his rounds as if nothing had happened.

Like the ghosts of lords and ladies long gone, Gerry and I would flit through the silent, empty rooms of the castle. We'd stand together in the great banquet hall, trying to visualise scenes of feasting and music and merry-making.

At the far end, peering up the enormous chimney tunnelling its way to the outside realities, we'd hold hands and dream a little. I'd feel very close to him then, but sometimes, when he kissed me, it felt as if he knew our dreams could never come to pass.

There was a cold, bright afternoon in late October when Gerry insisted on climbing right to the top of the tallest of the castle's seven towers. We stood there shivering, looking out over the vast tract of land thrown into sharp relief by the lowering sun, softened by the many fine old trees, oak and beech and chestnut, spreading out in all directions to the demesne walls.

"It's freezing up here, Gerry," I said after a while, but he seemed not to hear. He was tall and strong beside me, brooding and handsome, and I thought just then that I knew what being in love felt like.

"My people, the Caseys, came from over there," he said, pointing towards the southern boundary; "where the lake is. My father says his grandfather used to tell him that."

"Where the lake is?" I frowned; "I don't understand."

"It wasn't a lake then, only a bit of a stream cutting through their little fields. The Caseys, and plenty more besides, were driven out and their lands flooded and turned into a lake for the gentry to fish and boat on."

"The lake is man-made? I never knew that. God, it must have been awful for those poor people be driven off their lands like that."

"That's what me da says, anyway. There's talk now of this place being divided up and dished out to the local farmers, did you know that?"

He didn't wait for me to answer, but turned away and made

for the steps that would bring us down to the great hall again. The full implication of what he'd just told me didn't sink in until much later. I was too young and too wrapped up in what I felt for him that evening to comprehend the bitterness, perhaps even hatred, that had passed down the generations to him.

The irony of the fact that lands once occupied and worked by Gerry's forbears were now about to be handed over to the likes of my father, regarded locally as relatively well off (certainly by the Caseys), was lost on me. So too was the fact that it could be argued that the straitened circumstances in which Gerry's family now found themselves could be linked to cruel and inhumane events seldom mentioned anymore.

But perhaps some part of me, as I followed him down those steep, dark steps, did understand. When we emerged through the low opening into the light again and I saw him striding ahead of me across the bare, echoing boards as if he could no longer bear to be near me, I dashed after him and flung myself into his arms.

I kissed him in a way I'd never done before, deeply and fiercely and with an intent I had no real understanding of. And when at first he didn't respond, I kissed him all the more fiercely until I felt the desired effect take root in him, until he took off his jacket and spread it out on the ancient timbers beneath us and I lay down with him for the first time.

We still continued to come to the castle for a while after that. But nothing was ever quite the same for us again. The evenings were drawing in and I had my studies to attend to. As the days shortened further, the distancing between us grew, and gradually there came mutual acceptance that it was a gulf wider than we could hope to bridge.

"I'd better be off, Mrs. Foley," I said, rising now, knowing my mother would already be thinking of sending my father against me in the car.

"Well, you're a lovely wee girl, so you are. You must call again soon and we'll have the cup of tea and another chat. You'll be welcome anytime, you know."

Mrs Foley accompanied me to her front gate and held my bicycle for me as I put on my coat and gloves.

"Mind yourself on that bike, won't you, child," she said, regarding me with what seemed a curiously intent look of concern.

I thanked her for her kindness and mounted up. I had no inkling at all that evening, when I looked back and saw her still standing there waving, of what I suspect she had already guessed. Little did I know that, like the blast that blew our castle to smithereens, an explosion of fury and recrimination that would soon tear my life apart.

Perhaps it was as well that I didn't know, as I pedalled furiously for home, that the scandal which was about to break around me would fuel talk and gossip for months to come, while the destruction of something beautiful, but entirely unappreciated, faded quietly from memory.

Memories

An Féar Bán

By Dr. James Finnegan,
Letterkenny, Co. Donegal

A recollection from childhood of a brave little girl who has left a lifelong impression

RECENTLY, I visited Ferbane in Co Offaly. At a stretch, I guess one could say that Ferbane is not too far from the centre of Ireland, being about 16 kilometres south of Athlone on the road to Birr. The Irish for Ferbane is An Féar Bán – The White Grass, named after the local white bog cotton of the Bog of Allen.

Ferbane is both a picturesque village and a small town, and my mother, who is originally from Dublin, lives there. The local people are very friendly with a great sense of humour and community. Any time I am down town, someone always asks me how mum is and often end the conversation with, "Be sure to tell your mum I was asking for her."

On this recent visit, I decided to walk from my mum's home to my old secondary school which is now an occupied house about 800 metres outside the town boundary.

I took the route I used when walking to school in the mid-sixties, apart from the addition of a new section which bypasses the town centre. In our school days we often made the mad dash home at lunchtime, having pre-arranged the loan of a bike at the eleven-o'-clock break.

This particular mild dark January evening I was getting some fresh air after a small evening meal. As I strolled at a comfortable pace to the school, one memory, in particular, held my heart in a magnetic pull, as death tends to do, especially the death of a lovely young girl.

Mary Pat Daly, who was a few years younger than me and my classmates, would walk past us in the opposite direction heading to the local girls convent. The fact that Mary Pat had been diagnosed with leukaemia created, certainly for me, a feeling of sacredness and respectful hush as we passed by, offering a gentle and caring "Hello,"; and stepping off the pavement, if appropriate.

I marvelled that she could continue to courageously go to school when she knew she was going to die shortly. My impression of Mary Pat was that she was a gentle, loving girl full of tender humanity. Her parents being friendly with my own parents made me all the more sensitive to Mary Pat's ordeal.

A number of months after the diagnosis, Mary Pat looked very thin. Eventually she stopped going to school. This was followed by a long silent wait. Then we heard the news. A few friends and I were asked to carry the coffin. We were told that this was a special request from Mary Pat's parents. I, for one, was moved that we were held in such high regard and chosen for such an honour.

This was one of those treasured occasions in one's teenage years where defence-mechanisms fall away for a while and one truly recognises that one is valued and loved as one is. But there is another aspect to this, Mary Pat helped us to see ourselves more clearly as we were – young men capable of kindness, respect, gentleness and a genuine love of one's neighbour.

The memory of Mary Pat has visited me quite a number of times, especially over the last two years since I have retired and have a little more time for reflection. It's always a memory which stirs a deep feeling of compassion in me. I recognise and do not forget the beautiful brave individual human life that was Mary Pat. No doubt, her wonderful parents loved her dearly, nurtured her, and took great care of her.

Once or twice I met Mary Pat when I was on my own, walking back to school. I approach her with profound respect and some degree of awe, as if one were meeting a wounded bird of flight or, dare I say it, another Christ.

I walk by her and gently say, "Hello Mary Pat," and if I listen very, very carefully I can just about hear her faintest whisper in return, spoken softly, just like the soft white bog cotton of An Féar Bán,

'Hello James.'

Short Story

A Bit of Craic

By Ben Ritchie
Downpatrick, Co. Down

'Quiet Ned' is persuaded to tell his female work colleagues about the time he visited a fortune teller just to collect some friends and the startling revelation she made about him and his origins ...

IT WAS LUNCHTIME at Andersons Stores. The staff members were in the small, neat kitchen at the rear. Two ceiling lamps just about managed to keep out the leaden grey of a winter's day, but could do nothing about the rain's rhythmic beat against the condensation covered window.

Around the oil cloth covered table sat Alice, Beth, Bernie and Ned. The sandwiches had been eaten so now the remainder of the tea was being sipped as the three women discussed the forthcoming weekend. Ned was reading through the local paper.

"Sure, it will be a bit of craic," said Beth, "when's the last time a fortune teller came anywhere near here?"

"I don't know," replied Alice, the youngest of the three, "me ma would go mad if she knew. She's very religious and doesn't hold with that kind of stuff."

"Aye," added Bernie, "and who knows what she'd tell you?"

"That's the whole point," Beth continued, "We want to know what she can tell us." Then with a smile on her face she added, "She might even tell you if you were right to get engaged to Michael."

Bernie blushed and held out her left hand, allowing the weak light to bounce off a diamond ring, which was scarcely a week old. "I don't need a fortune teller to tell me that," Bernie replied, in a soft dreamy voice. The other two looked at each other in mock desperation.

The discussion went on for another few minutes but it was clear nothing was being decided. Unexpectedly Beth said, "Have you ever been to a fortune teller, Ned?" and just as unexpectedly he replied, "I have." He never looked up from the paper, but he had their full attention. Ned wasn't the type who went in for fortune telling.

"Well?" asked Beth expectantly.

Again without looking up from the paper Ned replied: "There are some things you're better off not knowing." This intrigued the women all the more.

Alice reached over, touched his arm and asked, sincerely, "Was it something bad, Ned?"

For the first time Ned looked up. "It's kind of you to ask, Alice. You're a lovely girl. If I was twenty years younger..."

"If you were twenty years younger," interrupted Beth, "you could be her Da instead of her Granda."

Now Alice blushed, but keeping a straight face Ned replied, "Beth, you've got very hurtful since you turned thirty." Beth sat back with a face of thunder and the other two tried to hide their smiles. They all knew that Beth and Ned's daughter had been best friends since primary school, and Ned's daughter was only twenty six.

Ned went to go back to reading his paper, but Beth hadn't spent all that time in Ned's house without learning a few things about this loveable rogue.

"Ah, come on Ned, tell us what happened. Sure we have to open the shop soon. You can't just leave us on tenther hooks. Please?" He looked up and saw her innocent face and big brown eyes.

Ned closed and folded the paper. "On your head be it," said Ned, "but you must swear that what's said here will never be repeated." The seriousness of his tone and the anxious look on his face shocked the women. This wasn't the Ned they knew. The wind started to howl outside. They all nodded and waited.

"It was years ago," he began," I had only been going out with my Bridie for a couple of months. She was still training to be a nurse up in Belfast. One night she and a couple of friends went to see a fortune teller. I was to pick them up about nine. I forget where it was.

"Anyway, it was a dark, wet November night and when I

eventually found the house it was out in the country, miles from anywhere. If it hadn't been for the kitchen light I would have missed it altogether.

"As I knocked on the door I could hear the rain rattling on the roof, which must have been tin. A young girl, who turned out to be the fortune teller's daughter, opened the door and invited me in.

"I'm here to collect Bridie and her friends," I explained.

"Of course you are," she replied," you're expected."

Bernie gasped, "Even the daughter had the gift."

"Or," interrupted Beth, sarcastically," Bridie had told them that Ned was coming to collect them."

Ned continued on in full flow. "As I walked into the room an old woman, sitting by the fire said, "Ah, here's Ned come for his Bridie."

"Ten out of ten'," for I was thinking like you, that it was all a bit of a con and that Bridie or one of her friends had told the old woman that I was coming. She mustn't have liked my tone, for next she says,

'You've come for Bridie tonight, Ned, but not long ago you would have been coming for Mary.'

"Well that stopped me in my tracks, because I had been going out with Mary about six months before I met Bridie. The old woman smiled contentedly while Bridie gave me one of her looks and poor Mary didn't know where to look.

"Rather than stand there like a lost sheep I went over to shake her hand. As our hands touched I noticed that the smile was replaced with a look of nervousness, maybe fear. Then she said, 'Excuse me sir, I meant no offence.'

"Well you could have blown me down with a feather. I looked at Bridie and her friends. They looked at me. Even the daughter at the door was looking surprised. Before I had time to gather myself the old woman guided me to an empty chair and was pouring me tea.

"When she sat down again she looked at Bridie and said 'You have a man who will protect you and your children, long life to you both.'

"There was a bit of an embarrassed silence after that. Marriage and children had never crossed my mind at that stage, and I didn't want anyone putting ideas into Bridie's head.

"Then the fortune teller turned to me again and began, 'You are a leader of men, who is equally happy in the company of others or is quite content to be on your own. You will always provide for yourself and your family. Sometimes you feel that you are different from other people, but you don't know why.'

"How do you know that?" I asked, totally taken by surprise.

She replied, 'Sometimes it is best not to know everything.'

'Well I want to know,' said Bridie, with a smile on her face, 'if I'm going to marry him and have his children, I want to know what I'm getting myself into.'

The old woman thought for a while.

'Very well. Ned, when I shook your hand I sensed the power in you, and then I saw it in your jaw. All human jaws are the same, but you have a thicker lower jaw just there, just below the ear. You have the jaw of a wolf.'

'There you are Bridie", said Mary, 'it's not children you'll be having, but a litter of pups.'

"The old fortune teller's gaze swept around the room, like a scythe in a hay field. No one spoke or laughed. She continued, 'Generations of generations ago when there was a power and knowledge that we have forgotten, there were people who took on the characteristics of animals. You, Ned, are descended from one of those people. That's why you feel different, and that's why, Bridie, he will protect and provide for you and your family. I cannot force you to keep this knowledge to yourselves but I advise you to do so. There may be others out there for whom the wolf is an enemy to be hunted down. Now go, it's late.'

"With that we were ushered out of the house and on the way home Bridie made the rest of them swear that they'd never tell anyone what they'd heard. She said she didn't want to be the laughing stock of the hospital – the nurse going out with the werewolf."

Just then the wind howled again, lashing rain at the window. Ned sat back from the table, his story over. Alice, Beth and

Bernie just looked at him. It couldn't be true but Ned had been so sincere while he was telling the story. They didn't know what to say. Eventually, the silence was broken by Alice.

"Ned, are you some sort of werewolf?"

He smiled. "No dear. Werewolves only exist in the movies."

Bernie asked a more reasoned question.

"If you're a leader of men, how is it that you work in the hardware department in Anderson's, when surely you should be some high powered businessman or a millionaire?"

Ned sighed, "When I did get round to asking Bridie to marry me she said that she wanted to, but that she wouldn't because she didn't want any children we might have to suffer or be made fun of, because of my *condition* . So I promised her that I would be like everybody else and that I wouldn't draw attention to myself in any way.

"We got married and thankfully have four daughters, because the wolf's jaw is only passed on the male side of the family. It ends with me. So I'm quiet Ned, who works in the hardware department, and I wouldn't have it any other way because Bridie is all I ever wanted."

Alice and Bernie had tears in their eyes at this stage.

"For goodness sake," broke in Beth," this is Ned, Our Ned, we're talking about. He can tell you the best wire to keep the fox out of your chicken pen but he's not any kind of wolf man." She glared at the other two, silently challenging them to disagree.

"How do you persuade a Doubting Thomas?" Ned asked to no one in particular. Alice and Bernie looked confused, while Beth sat back, arms folded.

"Touch your jaw below the ear," said Ned

"Why would I do that?" asked Beth warily.

Ned replied quietly, with an unnerving confidence, "Then you can touch mine and compare the two. Maybe then you'll believe me."

Alice's and Bernie's looks silently stated, *"That seems fair enough."* Realising that she didn't really have much of a choice if she wanted to maintain the high moral ground, Beth gently felt her lower jaw with the fingers of her right hand.

As she did so, Ned leaned across the table, anticipating her next move. Looking Ned straight in the eye she reached out slowly, her hand shaking just a little. Ned leaned in further. Just as Beth's fingertips brushed over Ned's stubbled skin he growled, snapped at her and let out an almighty wolf's howl, "oooooOOOOOO!"

Immediately there was a mixture of gasps and shrieks. All three ladies pushed away from the table and would have fallen off their seats only the wall was behind them. At the same time Ned deftly swivelled on his chair, sweeping the paper up as he went, and was halfway out the door before Beth took her first breath. As he was pulling the door closed he heard,

"Ned Callaghan! You're nothing but an 'oul..." He didn't hear the last word because something thumped into the back of the door, probably a lunchbox. Ned pressed his ear to the door and heard the beginnings of laughter punctuated with threats of revenge and his untimely demise. He smiled to himself, saying, "Sure it's only a bit of craic."

Memories

My World War I Ghost

By Martin Malone
Athy, Co. Kildare

A childhood gift of a World War1military helmet over forty years ago sometimes leads to speculation about the life and times of the man who wore it in the trenches

THE HELMET has been with me for 43 years, give or take some relatively short separations. For a while it hung on a ceiling beam in my brother's pub in Castlebar, alongside a Gurkha kukri knife and some other military memorabilia.

I was about 13 when my grandfather called round by appointment to an old woman's house in Cardiff, to replace a window in her bathroom. I can't recall her name, but we got along very well.

While my grandfather mixed putty and set to the job, she showed me her late husband's military sword, told me that he had served with the Engineers in World War I. She said when he got home he never spoke about the war, and she never pressed him to discuss it. He used to be such a smiler, she said, but that was before he went to France.

Before leaving her house, she handed me his helmet and insisted I take it, after I'd declined. I didn't think it right, but she was determined.

"Now, love...it's yours," she said.

I think now, looking back, that my grandfather wouldn't accept payment for his labour, and she was too proud to accept his offer. Instead, she paid by way of paying me in kind. So, I walked down the street, with the chin strap over my shoulder and the helmet tipping against my upper back.

A dirt-brown World War Mark I, it wears a dent, a bruising of metal, and I often wonder if it deflected shrapnel or a piece of flying debris from the wearer, or if there is perhaps some other more mundane reason for its existence. But I prefer to think that the helmet saved a skull from harm.

The helmet has been with me through the brightest and darkest days of my life. A ghostly, yet tangible object that at times I think to get rid of, to donate to a military museum, and perhaps that is where it will eventually end up.

But prior to that happening, I've decided that it's high-time to get to know the man who owned the helmet, the person who wore it in the trenches of World War I. He was an engineer – did he build bridges, lay mines...what sort of work did he do back in Wales, did he have children? There is so much that I don't know about the helmet's origins.

Through resources on the internet, I know the helmet was manufactured in 1914, that it is described in relevant websites as being a World War Mark I helmet, the earliest prototype – it matches the photographs displayed on the internet: brown in colour, leather chin strap, leather cross-section holding a crown of fibreglass in situ, netting under its black lining.

My helmet smells of its age – of dust, stale perspiration, old leather, which is frayed and worn

Under its rim is a hallmark, something like an A and definitely a H. Also, in red, the owner's rank and name... Lt for Lieutenant; J, his initial, and Tomlinson, his surname. There is another word but it's illegible. I think, though, it may read Captain, which if my guess is correct, means that my man had been promoted. For valour, I wonder, or simply a move up the ladder, to step into the shoes of his comrades who'd been killed or wounded in action?

I have a name for my helmet; it's properly known as a Brodie type helmet, called after its designer. But I call it 'J.' Over a million of these were manufactured, the demand driven by the astonishing amount of manpower lost through head wounds – soldiers prior to the introduction of the iron helmet used to merely wear cloth caps and these afforded no protection against winging bits of steel and stone.

There is a British Forces website that reveals a list of all of the Tomlinsons who served in that World War. There are loads of J. Tomlinsons. I have the feeling that I'm soon going to know a little bit more about my man, so I've decided to wait it out a little...just to whet the appetite.

Sometimes, I ask myself why that old woman gave a First World War helmet to a boy whom she didn't know. I can't remember her first name, and I'm annoyed that I have only scant recollection of what we talked about over tea and plain digestive biscuits. Annoyed, too, that I hadn't paid much attention to the framed photographs on the walls and mantelpiece, that I left her house carrying much and yet, paradoxically, so very little.

I'd reason to think of the First World War when I was in Iraq with the UN – we drove through the Iraqi army's deep, muddy trenches – not unlike those of 1914. Their serpentine way wider than a country road and deep enough to stack fifteen coffins on top of each other.

I occasionally think of J's hands gripping the rim of his helmet, of him adjusting his chin strap because the helmet didn't sit right, a common problem; and the friction rash the movement caused. I think of the fear in his eyes, the torment under that iron hat – a thousand and one thoughts fusing into a single prayer to survive, to get home, to re-discover his smile.

I hope that he did, at least sometimes, produce that smile, in spite of having been told that he didn't.

Short Story

Love on the Line

By Margaret Doherty
Raphoe, Co. Donegal

Jim strikes up a relationship with the telephone operator who has to take his special call every evening, but he reacts badly to a shocking revelation and it all comes to a halt ...

JIM LOOSENED his tie and tilted his chair onto its back legs, both actions he knew irritated the manager. He turned the handle on the phone to place his daily call to head office, unaware his life was about to change.

"Operator; how may I direct your call?" asked an unfamiliar voice.

"Dublin 31724, please."

"All our lines are busy sir. Will you hold or would you prefer to try again later?"

"I'll hold. You're new aren't you?"

"Yes. Did I do something wrong?" she asked nervously.

"Nothing wrong, textbook in fact. No, it's just the others all know I have to make this call every evening so I have to hold. They don't bother to ask."

"I'll remember that for future reference, sir."

"What is the sir in aid of? I'm a bank clerk, not your headmaster. My name's Jim. You can remember that for future reference. What's your name?"

"We're not supposed to have personal conversations with the subscribers," she replied, although she'd already noticed that was one of many rules her colleagues didn't pay much attention to.

"Forget what you learned in operator school, you're in the sticks now. The customers spend most of their time holding and it's your job to chat to us and distract us from how long it takes to get connected, so what's your name?"

"I'll come back to you sir when I have a line for you." Her

words were still formal but the tone had changed, it was lighter, as if she was smiling to herself. She would tell him her name, but not yet. He must wait. The operator always keeps you waiting. He was intrigued by this prim girl of the unknown name.

She answered his call every day and by the end of the week she revealed her name was Ella, but very little else. Her accent was impossible to place. It was a bit like a posh Dublin accent but she said she wasn't from Dublin, although she had gone to school there. She was easy to talk to and soon she knew all about him, how he hated his job in the bank and being away from the city.

The daily chats went on and on. They were the highlight of Jim's day. He had leave to take but he didn't want even a day off work. Before encountering Ella he lived for the weekends, but now he hated Saturdays and Sundays because he didn't get to speak to her and the pubs and discos he used to enjoy held no attraction for him.

His friends became concerned at his change from a carefree man about town to almost a hermit. He couldn't explain to them that he had somehow fallen in love with a girl he had never met. His head told him that his obsession was irrational, even insane, but his heart insisted she was his destiny, the only one for him.

Every week he asked her to go out with him to a dance, the pictures, a meal or anywhere she wanted but every week she refused. She hinted at a boyfriend back home but he knew she was making that up. Because he had nothing to focus on but her voice, he knew when she was lying.

There had to be a reason. He decided she must be ugly, afraid to let him see her. He thought of everything – a hare lip, a defacing birthmark, grossly overweight - but nothing dissuaded him. He loved her so it didn't matter what she looked like and he decided to tell her that.

He told her and it did provoke her into telling him the truth at last, a truth he had never imagined and in shock he hung up the phone. If only he had said something, said anything, but his silence had said it all.

After a week of her refusing to speak to him he had to see

her, to explain that he didn't mean to be so callous. He made an excuse to leave work early and went to the telephone exchange. He walked up and down past the door as if he was on a one-man picket.

He stopped and smoked another cigarette, the last one in the pack of the twenty he had bought that morning. A pack of ten usually lasted him two days. He looked at his watch again, a quarter to six, only fifteen minutes until her shift finished and she would come out. He had already checked that she was at work today and that this was the only exit.

A short, plump girl turned into the narrow side street and approached the door, heading in for the evening shift. She looked at him suspiciously. "Are you waiting for someone?" she asked. "Yes I am," he admitted. Three short words were enough. She recognised him although she had never seen him before. It was a knack they had, recognising voices

"You want to see Ella, don't you?" she demanded. "Yes," he admitted again.

"You have some nerve, turning up here after the way you treated her. How could you have been so cruel? You know she doesn't want to speak to you. She hasn't picked up a call from the bank all week. We can't keep covering for her. It will be noticed and she'll get into trouble. Don't you think it's hard enough for her? Leave her alone. You should go, leave."

He had already thought of leaving. If she rejected him now he would, but he had to see her first; to see her at least once. "I'm waiting here until she comes out. She can't stay in there forever. Could you please tell Ella I'm here?"

The girl didn't answer him, just turned her back to him and went in the door. He could imagine the excitement her news would bring as soon as she went up the narrow stairs. Nobody would get a call answered while the operators advised Ella what to do.

Eventually the door opened and two girls came out, the one he'd spoken to earlier and another one he knew was Ella. He'd always assumed the soft voice was from a small person but she was tall, almost as tall as him and, unlike many tall women who stoop or round their shoulders, she stood straight.

She had long dark hair and wore no make-up on her pale face. When she had snapped with him she had shouted at him that no, she wasn't ugly, wasn't deformed, but that everybody said she was pretty. In fact she was beautiful, to his eyes anyway.

He tried not to look into her eyes but he couldn't stop himself. They were beautiful too, a blue-green colour; unusual but beautiful.

"I need to talk to you alone. Please ask your friend to leave."

"I'm not leaving her alone with you," the friend insisted.

Ella turned to her. "We can go to the tea-shop, Bernie. We should both be safe there with Mary."

"Okay," said the friend throwing a dirty look at Jim before she went back upstairs. Ella silently led the way towards a small cafe at the end of the street. Jim held the door open for her, as he would for any woman, and she sat at the first table. The owner came over.

"Another day's work finished, Ella? What are you having?"

"A cup of tea and a scone, please, Mary."

"Tea for two is it?" Mary asked Jim, scrutinising him carefully. Although she hadn't seen him before, she could guess who he was. The telephonists gathered here, gossiping, and she mothered those away from home for the first time so she would know all about him.

"Yes. Tea for two and I'll take a scone too, please."

As soon as Mary left the table he tried to think of something to say. He'd rehearsed it often enough but it felt odd to start. The operator always speaks first. "I'm sorry," he blurted out. "I shouldn't have hung up on you. That was a terrible thing to do. It was pure shock, I didn't mean it."

"I'm sorry too. I shouldn't have told you like that. When I realised you were serious I should have written to you, explained everything."

"It doesn't matter. I've had time to think. I still want to go out with you. I don't see... I mean I don't understand ... why we can't."

"No Jim, you don't see. You don't know what it would be

like, how difficult it would be for you. There would be people staring, talking about us."

"I don't care. Let them talk, if that's all they have to talk about. I want to be your boyfriend."

Mary came back with the tea and scones. She put Ella's in front of her and moved the butter and jam to her right side as if she did it for all her customers. When she left again Jim remarked, "She likes you, doesn't she Ella? Everybody likes you."

"Everybody is very good to me. The girls at work are so protective, as you saw with Bernie, but sometimes it's as if they think I'm a china doll and might break in half, but I'm tough. I had to learn to look after myself.

"I have to be tougher than any of them, just like I have to be better at my job than any of them; I never have a crossed line or a dropped call. I'm like those new automated exchanges they are putting in. Soon your call to Dublin will only take a few seconds, no operator."

"What will you do then?" he asked, realising the advance everybody else was looking forward to would put her out of a job.

"I don't know. I have a permanent position so they'll have to find me something. The others will get moved to various departments but the likes of me will probably be stuck in a corner somewhere and forgotten about.

"I've heard about new jobs in something called telesales where you ring people up and try to sell them stuff over the phone, so I might try that."

"You would be great at that Ella, I'd buy whatever you were selling."

"You're just one," she said, smiling for the first time. Her face changed. The serious mask fell away and Jim knew he would be happy if he could see her always smiling.

"I could leave the bank and we could set up one of those telesales companies with loads of unemployed telephonists. We'd make a fortune."

"You're crazy, Jim. You know nothing about it. A minute ago

you'd never heard of telesales."

"Neither has anyone else, we'd be streets ahead of the competition. Anyway, can we forget about the telesales idea for now and just be friends again? I can't sleep or eat since we fell out. I'm going crazy, not able to think of anything except you.

"Please come out with me on Saturday night. I don't care what people say and if you are as tough as you say you are, you won't care either. Why should we throw away our chance to be happy together?"

"For someone who can't eat, you made short work of that scone! It's not that simple, Jim."

"Yes it is. It's very simple. We go out somewhere, we hold hands, I bring you home, I kiss you. We take it from there. Please say 'Yes' Ella; just one date. If it doesn't work out, then fine, but at least give me a chance."

"Okay," she relented at last, "Just one date. No promises. I'll meet you at the cinema, Saturday night at ten to eight."

He grinned with delight and relief. "I could pick you up," he suggested.

"No. I'll meet you there. Don't be late because I won't wait. I must go now, my landlady will be getting worried."

He stood up to help her but before he could offer she said, "I can manage," and picked up her white stick.

Short Story

The Escapee Granny

By Margaret Cameron
Old Hollywood Road, Belfast

Maureen is eighty six but she still cherishes the freedom of having her own home. However, others are concerned about her well being and safety and feel they must do what they think is right ...

I HAD SPENT HOURS, days in fact, since I was put in there planning to get out. It really was simple in the end; I just walked out when someone's visitors were coming in. I can't believe it, I'm free!

My heart is beating fast but I get a buzz that gives me the energy and drive to go for it. I suppose that's how prisoners feel when they decide to go over the wall. It's a great feeling, sort of fuelled by fear and the dream of freedom.

I have experienced that buzz before, the time I escaped from hospital. Being sent to hospital started all this. I could have managed all right on my own. Interfering old neighbours sent for the doctor. Then all hell was let loose with Social Workers arriving and gawking all around my flat.

I shouldn't have let the doctor in. I admit I had got down in health and hadn't been eating or taking the repeat tablets delivered by the chemist. There was a mound of them and the doctor clucked about that. The Social workers tut-tutted about the food in the fridge being out of date and the mess of the kitchen. If you're not eating, of course the food gets out of date. These la-de-da ladies treat you like an old 'has-been'. In my heyday I could have taught them a trick or two.

The ambulance arrived before I could get rid of them and I was carted off to hospital. They said I was dehydrated. There wasn't a thing wrong with me; given a few days I would have been back on my feet.

I was up every morning, dressed and ready to go home but the nurses said they had to do tests. There I was sitting around doing nothing. I could have been away on the bus. The bus pass is great. I spend my days travelling about. The buses are warm and comfortable and when I get to wherever I am going, I get a cup of tea and a bun. I rest a while and then I take the bus home again.

While sitting in the hospital, I kept thinking about what I was missing outside and after a few days I felt a bit fitter. I took a notion I would walk out and I did. No one noticed as I went through the double doors and down a corridor; the bolder you are the better. I was tense and kept expecting a hand on my shoulder to drag me back.

You feel on a high the further you get and then I saw 'Exit' and I was out. My flat wasn't that far from the hospital so I walked it. I was on cloud nine but when I got home I was exhausted, done in.

Pounding on the door woke me up from a wee nap. In the end I opened it, as I didn't want it put in. This big jolly fellow tucked my arm in his and I went with him to the ambulance. He was good fun. He said I should be in a film as the 'Escapee Granny.'

Anyhow, there I was back in hospital again. The nurses watched me like a hawk and then all these people came to talk to me. I didn't know whether they were doctors, social workers or psychiatrists. They asked me silly questions like "Who is Rory McIlroy?" I said, "A singer."

This big woman took me to a kitchen and said she wanted to see me make a cup of tea for myself, but I just sat down. They asked me if I would agree to a woman coming into my flat every day to assist me. I said, "Would you like some woman coming into your house?"

Then my two daughters arrived over from England. They are married with families of their own and they know I can manage on my own. I was delighted to see them and thought they would sort things out for me and that I would get back to my flat, but I didn't.

I didn't think they would do that, put their own mother in a residential home. I pleaded with them to take me home but

I was talked down; I would be better in a Home, it was for my own good, I was too frail to look after myself and they didn't want something to happen to me.

"Mum, you are eighty six and you are roaming about shopping centres in the evenings and taking lifts home. We are worried about you."

I only took a lift home once, well maybe twice. In the evenings when I felt lonely, I often went to the shopping centre and took a trolley so I could lean on it, and then I could walk around looking at things. One night I was waiting at the bus stop to return home and a nice man stopped and gave me a lift home. He said he had noticed me at the checkout. His wife was there too. I never should have told my daughters about the kind man.

The next thing I knew they were taking me to see this nice place and having afternoon tea. I was glad to get out of the hospital and went with them, but I had a sense of foreboding. I was trembling inside. Then they pulled up at this big house and I saw the words Residential Home.

I cried but they coaxed and hustled me out of the car and into the Home. Everyone was all over me; how glad they were to meet me and to show me my nice room. My daughters cooed about the lovely bed cover and the curtains. The room was nice but it wasn't my own wee bedroom. My daughters had it all sewn up - I would be well looked after with my food made for me and I wouldn't be lonely any more as there were lots of people about. The staff would see that I took my tablets and life was just going to be a ball, according to them.

It is dreadful being at the mercy of others, including your own; you just have no say in matters concerning your own life. All the comforts in the world don't replace one's freedom. Sometimes I wonder if this really is me.

They stayed around for about a week and came to visit every day and brought me little things from my flat, like photos and ornaments, to make me feel at home. Feel at home, my foot!

So that's how I came to be imprisoned in that home, and

'imprisoned' it was as you can't get out without knowing the numbers to press on a wee box on the wall. I tried several times to get close to whoever was going out to see if I could pick up the numbers but the staff always led me away.

I don't know how long I was in there. Every day seemed the same. Going for our meals was the big event of the day. Sometimes I sat with the others in the sitting room and one of the staff sat with us, like a shepherd minding sheep. At times we knitted but I didn't know what I was supposed to be knitting. Often I got fed-up and pulled the needles out and wound up the wool. It passed the time.

In bed at night I couldn't get to sleep as the thoughts pattered through my head like mice scuttling to and fro. Sometimes my heart pounded and I panicked.

I wished Tom were still alive. He wouldn't have let this happen to me. When he died my daughters wanted me to live with them in England. But what sort of life would that have been? Passed around like a parcel from one to the other. You should never give up your home.

Was I to be in here to the end of my days? I asked myself, like waiting to die? I decided I was getting out.

So here I am, free!

I have to get away quickly from the Home. My breathing is rapid but it has sharpened my wits. I go down under the trees to a main road. I don't know where I am but I see a bus pulling in at a stop and I get in amongst the people and a man helps me on. But I can't find my bus pass and the busman says crossly, "Take a seat Missus," and someone helps me to a seat.

After a wee while I get off the bus with others. I still don't know where I am, nothing looks familiar and I don't want to ask anybody. Suddenly I feel tired and I lean against this wall for a moment. My legs are a bit shaky and I am so cold and now I need to spend a penny. I see this pub restaurant and I go in. It is gloomy inside. The barman points me to the toilet and when I come out I head for this big coal fire. I sit down in a big soft armchair by the fire and oh, it is so cosy.

I just want time to think. It wouldn't be wise to go near my flat but where could I go? I must check in my handbag to see if I can find any money.

"Can I get you anything?" the barman asks, standing over me with his tray. I get a glass of water and he leaves me in peace.

Maybe I could get a taxi to Molly's house, she would let me stay. Her address must be in my bag. I'll look in a wee minute; I'll just rest for a moment.

I feel a hand on my shoulder shaking me and hear a voice saying, "Wakey, wakey."

I look up at two faces smiling at me. For a moment I can't remember who I am or where I am. One of the barmen says, "You've had a right wee snooze," and then they ask me if I'm waiting for someone. I need to get away before they become concerned so I tell them I'm going for the bus and make to get up but they sit me down again saying it's teeming outside and I haven't a coat.

"You'll be drenched. Can we get you a taxi?"

It seemed a good idea to get out, so I say yes and then they ask, "Where to?... Where do you live? ...Have you an address?"

"To Molly's house, she lives down the street at the side of the Curzon Cinema . I'll know it when I get there."

"The Curzon ...is it still there? That's a good bit away."

"Will you get me a taxi? Molly will pay for it."

He says he will and he goes away and the other barman says, "I'll get you a cup of tea while you're waiting." He brings this cup of tea and a big slice of Pavlova. I plunder in my handbag for my purse but he says, "It's on the house."

I was so glad of the cup of tea and lovely Pavlova . They are two nice big fellows and keep coming back and forth to talk to me. They ask me if I like Pavlova and the one called Sam says, "I made it especially for you." They are great craic. I keep asking about the taxi but they say the taxi firm is busy but it 's coming.

I am just finishing my tea when this woman says, "Hello,

Maureen, are these fellows looking after you? They don't give me tea when I come in."

I look up into the smiling face...and then I see the peaked cap and dark uniform.

"Ah, no," I plead; "I just want to go home."

Memories

Those Winter Sundays with David Copperfield

By Jean Tubridy

Tramore, Co. Waterford

Going back fifty years to family Sunday evenings in Co. Monaghan; mum and the two boys share a Dickens television treat while dad busies himself with domestic chores

THE HOUR from 5.20pm to 6.20pm on those winter Sundays in 1965, just as I was turning eight years old, still tick through my senses like the deep-throated tock-tock of the big wooden clock that hung in the kitchen of the Bank House on Main Street, Castleblayney, which was home back then.

The television was still a huge novelty and was severely rationed by our parents who feared we kids might become heavily addicted. The serialisation of Charles Dickens' *David Copperfield* was viewed rather differently to programmes like *Mr Ed* and *Crossroads*, and the fact that it was aired on Sunday evenings added to its parental appeal.

Dad would make sure that the fire was blazing in the drawing room so that mother, my brother and I would be nice and cosy while we watched the classic on the black and white television with its precious shiny knobs that I wasn't allowed to touch!

As we were transported to David Copperfield's England of the 1820s Dad took over the kitchen. While we were introduced to people like the kindly housekeeper, Peggotty, the nasty stepfather, Edward Murstone, and oddly-named landlord, Wilkins Micawber,

Dad would stoke up the Rayburn, which had drying towels hanging on its rail, and open the USA biscuit tin that housed his tidily packed assortment of wooden shoe brushes and tins of black, brown and tan polish. All our footwear were transformed from scuffed, mucky lumps back into glistening shoes fit to walk proudly into the Co. Monaghan world on Monday morning.

The ironing came next. While Dad was a cardigan and old slacks man at weekends, he was a dapper dresser when he was in his bank manager role. He was firmly of the view that no one could press a pair of trousers like he could, and he was probably right! He had special flannel cloths that he laid carefully over the trousers and then poured a perfect measure of water from his earthenware jug which hissed like a steam train when he firmly rubbed the red hot iron up and down the crease of each long leg.

I always loved the look of satisfaction on his face as he hung the newly-pressed trousers on one of his big wooden clothes hangers. I often got to see it as I raced down the two flights of stairs to the kitchen during the ads to get the glass of water that was really about drinking in the whole atmosphere of our bright, secure kitchen full of Dad, which was such a contrast to the scary, dark world of the young David Copperfield.

Sometimes, I'd find that he had already started to get the tea ready. This consisted of sandwiches made from the remains of the Sunday roast. Sunday lunch was a big affair in our house back then with roast beef, lamb or chicken, roast potatoes, baked potatoes, two vegetables and the essential gravy made with Bisto - *Bisto browns, Bisto seasons, Bisto thickens, all in one go*! (as the advert used to say).

Dad's sandwiches always had perfect symmetry. He relished the challenge of cutting a loaf of bread so that each slice was the very same delicate size. All crusts were removed and each sandwich cut into neat triangles and carefully placed on the big blue and white flowery china plate that he and Mother had got for a wedding present.

When we'd arrive in the kitchen as the Angelus bell was ringing out around Castleblayney, and still steeped in David Copperfield's trials and tribulations, we'd find Dad sitting at the table putting the finishing touches to his multiple entries to the Sunday Independent crossword competition.

He would cross the tiled floor in that waltzy way of his, boil up the kettle and make the first of what would be about three pots of strong tea in the silver teapot. Any stray tea leaf would be flicked back into the waiting caddy.

As we tore into the sandwiches he'd turn to me and say: "Well, tell me what David Copperfield was up to this week? You know it's a long time since I read the book but I'll never be able to thank my father enough for buying me that set of Charles Dickens to help me get through that terrible year I had pneumonia when I was twelve."

I'd do my best to tell him exactly what had happened and I can still see him listening intently with a slightly glazed look in his eyes. The pile of sandwiches would slowly dissolve and the tea would get stronger and stronger, just as I got more and more aware of the mingling smells of shoe polish, evaporating steam, hardening glue from the competition envelopes and the steeping porridge oats on the white cooker behind me.

Short Story

The Rush of Silver

By Oliver McBride
Downings, Co. Donegal

Sean gets a harsh lesson in the realities of fishing for salmon off the Donegal coast and any romantic notions of glamour or grandeur are soon dissipated

THE AFTERNOON saw the wind and waves rise. The little thirty-four foot half-decker boat started to bobble in the water. As the evening drew in a brisk June storm was blowing and Sean was hoping the Skipper was thinking of heading for home.

His father had told him that he was too young to be salmon fishing. The long days would numb a fifteen-year-old; sap his body, both mentally and physically. He was now at sea over fifteen hours and it looked like more to go.

He was cursing himself for being over-enthusiastic. He was missing school, he was missing his friends, he was missing properly cooked food and he was missing terra firma. Since breakfast at home in the early hours, nothing had seemed right. His father warned him but he could never have been prepared for the sheer boredom.

They had just shot the nets again. The tide was on the turn, so the Skipper said, and with the rising wind he was expecting a run of salmon. "There better be" thought Sean. Seven measly salmon all day; not what he dreamed off as he walked down the pier early that morning.

He was wakened that morning at three o'clock. In fact, he hadn't really slept with the excitement. This would be his first time fishing on a real big boat. No punting around in a currach, this was the real deal.

He had scoffed down his breakfast of porridge, homemade scone-bread and tea, lovingly prepared by his mother. She looked anxious as he stepped out the door but she called him back, kissed him on the forehead and blessed herself.

It was still dark but a little twilight was beginning to appear. The sky was clear and there wasn't a breath of wind. He walked the mile and a half humping his bag full of gear to the pier. When he got there it was a hive of activity with six other boats and crews scrambling around getting ready. His boat 'The Silver Spear' was tied on the outside of two others, her red paint reflected in the calm blue water.

The first order he got after he put his bag onto the boat was to go and get a drum of fresh water from the tap at the head of the pier. He then off-loaded fresh supplies off the back of a van belonging to the Skipper's brother. When everything was sorted it was just after four-thirty and the sky was climbing in the east, flashing brilliant wisps of red high into the atmosphere.

The boat engines roared into life smashing against the silent back-drop of the village, spewing harsh grey plumes of diesel smoke into the fresh air. Sean took his father's oilskins and wellies from his bag. He was given permission to borrow then until he could afford his own. The wellies were a good fit but the oilskins were a little long.

The boat engine roared to a deafening decibel. More thick and foul smelling diesel fumes breached the calm air as a louder roar came from the wheelhouse window as the Skipper gave the order to cast-off. Sean's two crew mates untied the ropes and jumped in.

The Skipper reversed the boat out until he was facing into the open bay and then they were off, steaming out to sea followed by a convoy of the five other boats; each rushing to catch the silver harvest.

That seemed a lifetime ago now. It was time again to start running up and down the drift net keeping an eye out for salmon striking the net. It was a priority to get the fish out of the net before the seals got to them. There were many seals stalking the boat. This morning, steaming down the bay, the Skipper said that he had spotted three heads following in their wake. His mood was not good. Paddy, Sean's crew mate, said that if you see three seal heads there is probably eight or nine in reality.

After the morning shoot, as the boat lay still on the water, Sean could see seal heads popping up-and-down all along the length of the drifting nets. Now and again the floats would sink but by the time they would get to the spot, there would be nothing left in the net but a salmon head.

"The calm weather is causing this" the Skipper complained. "The salmon won't run when the sun is so strong and any that does is getting picked off by the seals once they hit the net."

There was no movement in the water; no tidal drift and no wind drift as the sun rose towards the midday. Time dragged on. They had hauled and re-shot the nets several times and with afterwards the kettle was put down for tea. Andy, the other crew mate, made the tea. It was always cold, weak and unsatisfying, leaving Sean longing for the comfort of a home-made cuppa.

As they started another run up the nets, Sean was put on the half-deck up at the bow. At first he couldn't spot anything but soon his eyes became accustomed to the refraction between the surface and under it and eventually his eyes and senses became keen.

Around three o'clock they hauled the nets again and the Skipper ordered the dinner to be made. There were more boats coming into the vicinity and he wanted dinner early because the competition for good spots would be heating up as it came to the turning of the tide.

Sean still didn't feel too good since dinner. The tea and soggy sandwiches were bad but the dinner didn't settle. The heaving of the boat was leaving him feeling a bit seasick. He had put it down to the dinner. Andy had done his best but the little gas camping cooker was little more than useless. The potatoes were undercooked, raw in the middle. There was an attempt to fry sausages, which were cut up and dumped into lukewarm mushroom soup.

Sean was up again on the half-deck. The waves were breaking over the bow and he was past caring about getting wet. He was keeping a tight eye on the nets as the boat hopped along the nets. Paddy and Andy were busy pumping the boat again as she filled up with excess water.

All of a sudden he shouted "Salmon" waving his hand and pointing in the direction of where the floats had sunk.

The Skipper slowed the boat down as Paddy and Andy reached for the net using the boat hook. They hauled up the net and picked the fish out. The net was barely back in the water when Sean was shouting again. For the next two hours they worked hard up-and-down the nets as a run of salmon hit. Twenty-one salmon later and the nets were drifting dangerously close to the rocks.

One-and-a-half miles of hard man-hauling and another five salmon later the nets were onboard as the buoy drifted onto the top of a big washing rock. They had taken turns between the hauling and the picking but Sean's arms could barely haul the last one-hundred yards.

Now the sky was grey and black rain clouds began pounding down heavy rain. Sean watched the rain drops bounce off the sea water as the boats moved away from the rocks. He was wondering if the Skipper had decided to head home. Some of the other boats had now disappeared and he took it that they were heading for shelter. Not a chance!

"Get the tea on!" a booming voice came from the wheelhouse window.

"Your turn Sean," said Andy, nodding in the direction of the cabin.

"We're not heading in?" Sean asked his crew mates in hope.

"No way" said Paddy. "Not when there's a run on."

At least he was in shelter now watching the kettle trying to boil. They had steamed back out again and were shooting away again. By the time the Sean had the tea made the nets were reset and he balanced his way across the deck with a cuppa for the Skipper.

"Begob!" he said, "a hot cuppa at last! Think I'll make you cook from now on."

The good mood seemed to be infectious now the salmon were running. Everyone seemed a lot more cheerful.

"Looks like you're out of a job, Andy" Paddy said when Sean told him what the Skipper had told him.

"Do you hear me protesting," Andy laughed.

The next few hours saw them catching another thirty salmon. They hauled before sunset and the boat was beginning to feel dangerously heavy with the nets and salmon onboard. This time the Skipper moved further out from the shore as the night drew in. They shot away again and the salmon were put away under the floorboards of the false top-deck.

Paddy and Andy took the first watch as the boat was tied to the end of the nets and allowed to drift along. Sean and the Skipper took to the bunks for a sleep. As soon as he lay down his head he was out, despite the pitching and rolling of the boat. He was wakened sometime later by Paddy and scrambled out into the cool night air.

All hands on deck began to haul in the dark and another twenty salmon were picked out of the nets. The nets were shot away again and this time there was no room under the false-deck for the salmon so they were put into the cabin. Paddy and Andy took to the cabin for a sleep. The cold air kept Sean awake and when the boat rose on the waves he could see the lights of other boats off in the distance.

The time passed slowly and Sean was relieved when the Skipper told him to give his crew mates a shout to haul. He was hungry now and it was twenty-four hours since he was at home. As they began to haul, the hunger passed as another nineteen salmon were picked out of the net.

"Are we going again?" shouted Paddy to the Skipper.

"I think we'll risk a short one," the Skipper shouted back.

Sean could see Andy felt a little anxious like himself. It was rolling the dice and it seemed risky.

"Get the tea down" the Skipper shouted to Sean as the boat turned to head back out.

The sky was rising in the east. In fact, it had hardly set on the horizon all night even though the sky over the fishermen was black. The wind had also eased and to Sean's relief the sea had started to die down.

After the nets were shot and the tea taken, Sean and the Skipper tried to get their heads down amongst the numerous salmon that now filled the cabin. Next time he came out of the cabin the wind and sea was calm again. They made their last haul and the fifteen salmon were stored around the wheelhouse. This time there was no doubt that the Skipper was heading for home.

As they steamed slowly up the bay the boat was dangerously low in the water. They met the other boats who had headed for shelter the evening before steaming out and now the pier was deserted when the boat moored up. The van from the previous day came roaring down the pier. The van was emptied of grub and drums of diesel.

The salmon from the cabin and around the wheelhouse were loaded into the van. Then the nets were hauled onto the pier and the salmon lifted from under the false deck. Sean was sent to replenish the supplies onboard while this was going on. He was looking forward to his own bed but it wasn't to be. As soon as the nets were back on board the Skipper turned the boat around and they headed back out again to fish salmon.

ORIGINAL WRITING
FROM
IRELAND'S OWN

If you have enjoyed this collection of short stories and memoirs, and would like some more, we have some copies left of our previous publications for 2014, 2013, 2012, 2011 and 2010 at just €10 per copy, post and packing included.

2010

2011

2012

2013

2014

Contact:

Niamh Callaghan, Original Writing, SPADE Enterprise Centre,
North King Street, Dublin 7.
T - 01-6174834 • E - info@originalwriting.ie • W - www.originalwriting.ie